# THE DULUTH MONGOOSE

Daba & McDonald

# THE
# DULUTH
# MONGOOSE

## by
## Jack Denton Scott

*Man is immortal, sage or fool;*
*Animals end by different rule . . .*
*L. I. Guiney*

Illustrations by Lydia Fruhauf

WILLIAM MORROW & CO., NEW YORK, 1965

*Special Edition for the Arrowhead*
*Zoological Society, Duluth, Minnesota.*

for Mary Louise—*Io sono te, tu sei me.*

# ACKNOWLEDGMENTS

I would like to express appreciation for the cooperation of the Honorable Stewart L. Udall, Secretary of the Interior of the United States, to the Treasury Department, Bureau of Customs, and to C. L. Bingham, Assistant Collector of Customs, Duluth, to Mayor George D. Johnson and City Attorney Harry E. Weinberg of that city, and to Harold Grinden of Duluth's Chamber of Commerce—and especially to Lloyd Hackl, recently retired Director of the Duluth Zoo, and John Mealey, Magoo's caretaker. I also appreciate the help of the people of that city, and am grateful for Dora Mary Macdonald's excellent book, *This Is Duluth,* which was helpful in re-creating some historic touches of the city.

J. D. S.

# PART I

## *The Jungle*

THIS IS A MOSTLY TRUE STORY ABOUT A MONGOOSE named Magoo. He is the only one of his breed who is a legal resident of the United States, and he was given his name by a citizen of Duluth, Minnesota. The people of that city, and hundreds of other cities in America, also gave him his life, proving that right can still win out over might—in this case, the right of the people of the United States against the might of their Federal Government.

I first learned about Magoo from an Associated Press news item that appeared on Saturday, November 17, 1962, in more than three hundred newspapers. The story also carried a photograph of the Director of the Duluth Zoo with the mongoose perched on his shoulder.

It read:

### UNDESIRABLE ALIEN

Mr. Magoo, a mongoose given to the Duluth, Minn., zoo by a foreign seaman, faces destruction. A U. S. Fish and Wildlife

Service official pointed out a 1900 regulation forbids importation of the cobra-fighting animal because of its high reproductive rate. Unaware of the death sentence and the crisis swirling
over his head, the animal cuddles up here alongside zoo curator,
Lloyd Hackl . . .

Reaction was swift. Throughout the nation people took
up pens and telephones, sent telegrams, and made personal protests. For example, for one solid week the Duluth
Zoo received a telephone call every minute in defense of
the mongoose. The city of Duluth led the campaign in
the battle that followed between the people and what they
deemed a heartless bureaucratic government.

My interest was immediately captured. I had been to
India several times and knew and liked mongooses, an
appealing and courageous little breed that some of us first
learned about in "Rikki-tikki-tavi," Rudyard Kipling's famous short story which tells how a pet mongoose kills a
pair of cobras and saves the life of the English family he
lives with.

Kipling described him as "Rather like a little cat in his
fur and his tail, but quite like a weasel in his head and
habits. His eyes and the end of his restless nose were pink.
He could scratch himself anywhere he pleased with any
leg, front or back, that he chose to use; he could fluff up
his tail until it looked like a bottle-brush, and his war-cry

as he scuttled through the long grass was: Rikk-tikk-tikk-tikki-tchk!"

Some of us have heard about the mongoose through Harry Belafonte's calypso song, "The Sly Mongoose," as a cunning creature that knows how to take care of itself. But it is doubtful if many who rushed to Magoo's defense had seen or heard of a mongoose, or knew what an extraordinary animal it is.

Many of my friends in India keep mongooses as household pets, as we do cats. I have seen them scratch at the door to be let in, then rush for the best chair or closest lap, to curl up and sleep. An English couple in New Delhi had a pair that would come to you raising their heads to be petted, then sit up and beg for food. Many shops in Bombay, Delhi, and Calcutta also have mongooses in residence.

Magoo, the Duluth mongoose, is from the species *Herpestes nyula,* or *mungo,* known as the common Indian mongoose. In the wild I have often watched them sit up like miniature kangaroos, watching the sky. The South African species, the meerkats, spend hours in this position. In this stance they search for their enemies, the birds of prey, giving them time to scurry to their burrows before the birds pounce. But they are so courageous, such fierce fighters, that other than these birds, big cats, and large carnivora, they have few enemies. Indians have told me that foxes and jackals ten times their size will seldom do battle with a pair of mongooses, preferring to look for a less aggressive menu. The mongooses themselves are carnivorous, concentrating on reptiles, rodents, lizards, and almost anything running or flying that they can catch and conquer. They are respected in their native habitat for helping to keep down the hordes of rats and insects.

Wild mongooses return this regard, often leaving the jungle to live near villages and breeding litters of two to four that come as often as five times a year. It is not unusual to see a pair of mongooses promenading down a village road with their family two weeks after the young have opened their eyes, at the age of sixteen days. They are affectionate mates and protective and responsible parents, fighting anything that threatens their offspring, teaching them how to hunt, hide, fight snakes, dig burrows, and approach humans without fear.

Once, while I was sitting on a hummock in the Indian jungle waiting for a beat, a group of men to drive a leopard toward me, a female mongoose approached and sat up staring in my direction. After a few seconds, when she had determined that I wasn't going to cause any trouble, she chittered, a noise like someone rattling keys in his pocket, and two young ones came out of the underbrush and also sat regarding me.

They sat for ten minutes, and I could almost hear the mother tutoring, "This is a man. Usually they are our friends, but first you must watch and see if this human is friendly. Then you can approach."

And approach the young ones did, sniffing my boots and staying with me until the shouts of the men on the beat grew nearer and finally frightened them away.

Mongooses are affectionate and intelligent, and some people claim that they make even better pets and companions than dogs do. An Englishman wrote of owning one that retrieved the game birds he shot. But, being of higher intelligence than a dog, the mongoose first ate the portion that he liked, then dropped the rest in his master's hand, instead of bringing the bird directly back. Man and mongoose took long walks in the jungle, the animal came when called, liked music, and loved to smell flowers. He slept with his head on the pillow beside his owner.

The common Indian mongoose, the most popular of the six Indian varieties, probably because he was made a hero by Kipling, has a life span of eight years and comes from a large family which includes about thirty species. The mongoose's true home is Africa, with the greatest diversity of types there, including the zebra or striped, red, the large white-tailed, *Herpestes albicaudatur,* which reaches a twenty-six-inch length. One of the eight African species is found in Spain. The most unusual are the crab-eating, and a large mongoose that precariously dines on the eggs and the young of crocodiles. This one, the Egyptian mongoose, the ichneumon, often pictured on ancient carvings and tombstones, has been a valued pet since the days of the Pharaohs.

So this is an animal with a past, a presence, and a definite place in the scheme of things.

The story of the effort to save the life of the only mongoose in America actually had its beginning in a far-off place—perhaps with a wild peacock.

We don't know exactly how it began. The name of the sailor who brought Magoo into the United States has never been revealed. The act was a crime under U. S. law and thus even if we knew his name we wouldn't tell it. But anyone who has spent as much time in India as I has a good idea how Magoo came to another land, more than seven thousand miles from his native country.

I have lived in the jungle with the *Madia,* the forest people, observed wild mongooses on the roads and in the bamboo thickets, seen them being captured for pets or to be sold, watched them fight the snake charmers' cobras on the street corners of Bombay, Madras, Delhi, and Calcutta. And I think I know how this story started. No one can say that it did not happen this way. It has before, and will again.

.   .   .

It probably began in late May, 1962. I can see the sky that day like a vast blue sea awash with whitecap clouds, as it always is at that time of year. An eight-year-old boy, brown as a penny, was walking along a dusty jungle trail, looking for a lost goat. He was a boy like thousands of others I have seen in India, the land that holds one seventh of the human race, where one child is born every five seconds. And he lived in one of the 600,000 villages that lie across the subcontinent like beads in a flung necklace. Let's call the boy Sammar and let's say that he lived in the village of Mulni, deep in the jungles of India's central province, Madhya Pradesh, and that he was the son of Ramlal, an aboriginal, a Gond native.

Off the side of the road ahead of the boy a peacock, its plumage vivid in green, blue, gold, and bronze, was mincing into a growth of young bamboo, *ringal,* followed by three drab brown peafowl and a dozen russet pea biddies, chicks that were chirping like crickets as they vanished into the green tangle of jungle. Sammar, standing as still as the slender elephant-ear-leafed teak tree beside him, could see the peacock even in the thicket. The tropical sun struck its brilliant blue breast in a shimmer of reflected light.

He turned, carefully placing his bare feet on the path so

he would make no noise. When he was far enough away he broke into a run, entering the primitive mud-hut village out of breath. Sammar's home was a hut built on one side of a quadrangle; the other three sides were closed in by a cattle and a cart shed and by a crude granary. Framework was rough timber sunk into the ground. A shield of clay had been formed around the frame, and the roof was thatched with grass burned brown and hard by the sun. The walls inside were thickly sealed with buffalo dung, in the belief that it repelled insects. As he came into the single room he shouted, "Father! Father! *Mor!* A male, three females and many young!"

His father, a handsome oak-brown man in a loincloth, with brass rings gleaming in his ears, was sitting on the dirt floor, pounded iron-hard by use, honing an ax with a flat stone. It was the hand-forged crescent-shaped *kulhadi,* his principal weapon of defense. A deadly blade with a three-foot bamboo handle, it can be hurled with accuracy for twenty-five yards by an expert.

"Where, Sammar?"

"Not many steps from the River Tawa. Let us go! Shall I get the panther skins and the nets—"

"Near the Tawa, is it? You know the mor are wary. If they hear us they will fly the river."

This stopped his son for a moment. "Not so with these

chicks, Father. I don't believe they can fly until the next heavy moon."

Ramlal nodded thoughtfully. "This can be so. Also the forest contractor is coming soon from Itarsi to mark the bamboo that should be cut. He will buy the mor. You have done well. You may get the skins and the nets."

As so often happens to jungle people, where life is short, Sammar's mother had died an untimely death five years ago. Ramlal tried to fill the void by taking the boy with him on daily hunting and food missions. While having their *bhath,* a thrice-weekly meal of grain, a few vegetables, and small chilies, they talked often of life in the jungle and the daily struggle against wild animals and poverty. As a result, Sammar was older in outlook than most of the children of Mulni.

Like many a village boy who is close to his father, he hunted peacocks in the way of the elders. Peacocks are a symbol in India and much in demand commercially, despite their association with the Hindu religion. It is believed that one of the main gods of the Hindus, Shiva, had a son, Karttikeya, who rode Mor, a peacock, thus the bird is protected nationally as a sacred creature. But the jungle people, who are animists, worshipping the natural, rivers, rocks, trees, mountains, the sun and moon and sacred caves, have no such belief. They trap the peacock for the pot, or net it in an astonishing manner, to sell it alive to animal dealers or entrepreneurs like the forest contractor Ramlal mentioned.

Those of us who have seen Indians with peacocks in bamboo cages behind their huts and watched them walking along the roads with the gaudy birds in nets know that they bring needed rupees to the natives. I've watched animal dealers driving their hard bargains, paying six rupees (a rupee is about twenty-one cents) for an adult male and three for healthy young males. For the Gonds, who consider fifty rupees a year sufficient income, these are sums worth seeking.

Zoos are not the only interested customers. A handful of peacock feathers is an implement of conjuring, carried by most Indian mendicants and fakirs who claim skill in magic. The priests of sacred Benares use a wand of feathers to punish worshippers for their sins, or to absolve them. In the Punjab smoking a peacock feather in a pipe is an antidote for snake bite; the feathers are sold in many bazaars, with the guarantee that the ashes are a remedy for vomiting.

In southern India the rubbed-in fat of the peacock is believed to cure stiff joints. In some places its dung is said to cure eye diseases; the nomad Basuis (robbers and counterfeiters) carry a tuft of tail feathers to prevent detection.

In folklore a peacock warns the pretty maiden Bopoluchi that the man who is taking her to his house is not her uncle but a robber. Indian stories also tell of peacocks that are actually disguised warriors guarding the palaces of maharajas. The Gujarati say that if a peacock cries once when a person leaves for a foreign country it is a good omen for the acquisition of wealth; if the beautiful bird cries twice it means the traveler will gain a wife.

So the jungle dwellers are aware that the peacock is valuable. The problem is that the bird is both wary and a powerfully fast flyer, flushing at fifty to one hundred yards from its pursuer. But years of living in the jungle have taught the natives that the brainy bird has one weakness: the leopard, called a panther by Indians. The spotted cat fascinates peacocks. Many reliable observers have watched a crafty adult male peacock stand and stare, hypnotized, as a leopard crept up and killed it.

The forest people use this weakness. Once in a while they are lucky enough to kill a leopard by trapping it in a pit where it is impaled on sharpened stakes. Then they skin the cat, carefully tan the hide, and fashion a cloak. Camouflaged in this skin, creeping on hands and knees, a hunter can often get close enough to a peacock to net it. The net is an artfully constructed mesh, patiently woven by the village women from thin strips of green, pliable bamboo.

Now Sammar eagerly got the skins and two nets. This

was his favorite sport. Like most village boys, he liked to drape himself in the beige and black-rosetted hide and creep up on the birds. It is the nearest thing they know to play.

The sun, god of life, was high in his place, his stare causing sweat to roll in beads on the bare chests of Sammar and his father as they hurried along the Kesla-Bori road that wound past the whitewashed *dak* bungalow with its red tile roof that sat on a knoll at the edge of the village. These daks are the stopping places of the forest officers, who are much like forest rangers, and come to inspect the trees, caution the natives about fires, and plan reforestation.

Two of the forest officers had just left this dak, for this was a dangerous time of careless fires, as Ramlal and his son knew. Rain, goddess of fertility, had not dropped her blessing for many weeks, and the *gram* fields of Ramlal were scant. But like boys in forest villages everywhere in India, Sammar still guarded the grain fields by day from the hungry herds of white spotted deer, the chital, and the huge blue antelope, the blue bulls, which could gulp down an entire planting in one visit.

When boys like Sammar are not guarding crops, they are watching the buffaloes, goats, and cattle of their fathers. The cows are their most valuable possessions. Although they do not revere them as holy, as the Hindus do in *panch gavya,* the name for the five products that come from the sacred cow, they do depend upon the milk, butter, curds, urine, and dung. To protect their charges most boys carry a long, sweat-hardened staff of bamboo, depending upon it and their shrill voices to drive off leopards, jackals, foxes, and hyenas. The herd boys can often be seen after work, gathered in villages playing games, chasing dogs, or pitching stones in a small hole, their version of quoits.

But Sammar preferred the men of Mulni to the boys, and he was always around the campfire at night when sparks flew into the dark and the men talked to the two, now old and crippled, who had fought off a tiger one day when they were on a beat for some men who had come from Nagpur to hunt. For one rupee each the men of Mulni had agreed to walk abreast through the place in the jungle where the *shikari,* the professional hunter, said there was a tiger. The men from Nagpur sat with their rifles on a tree platform called a *machan.*

This day, the tiger, *sher,* the noble one, refused to run before the shouting men. He broke back through the line, knocking one man down. The man beside him came to his rescue. Together, with their crude axes, they fought the monster with its claws like skinning knives. But, bleeding and crippled, they lived, and the tiger fled. Every year they were honored with a ceremony that had dancing and singing, roasted goat, and much *mahua,* wine from the tree blossoms. For their bravery they held the status of headmen. A number of villages have men like these who are the boys' heroes. As the other boys did, Sammar thought, and sometimes acted out, how he would have faced the cat had he been a grown man.

Now on the road, the dust, pulverized into powder by buffalo-drawn carts, rose in smoky puffs as Sammar and his father hurried. They stopped briefly, as all the villagers did, at the curve where the crowns of the hills, Gitti Deo and Chumma Gondi, lifted from the horizon. They bowed their heads in piety to their two gods, then went on until they could hear the sigh of the River Tawa.

It was at this point a week ago where they had walked to the banks of the river and seen an ugly sight not uncommon in the Indian jungles. Eight *dhole,* the dark red, dangerous wild dogs, had an elklike *sambur* and her calf in the stream. They had already almost eaten the calf alive, and the mother was a rip of gaping wounds. Sammar and his father fought the dogs off, throwing stones and brandishing their axes until the marauders turned and trotted away. Sammar fled, crying, while his father ended the suffering of the sambur and her calf. Now as he remembered, he thought how strange that the gods would let a thing like that happen. He was saddened that the sound of the river as it ran in the sunlight brought this memory.

But now they were approaching the place where he had seen the sun flaming on the blue of the peacock. He slowed his pace, and touchingly adult in his earnestness, cautioned his father.

He put a finger to his lips for silence, knowing that the wary peacocks often rested, listening, in the shade of the heavy thickets, out of danger and the lance of the sun. Making a motion with his hand that to a Westerner signals to move away, but to an Indian means to approach, he led his father to the place where the ringal made its own small forest.

There they stopped and put on the leopard-skin cloaks and unfurled the nets; hunching over, they moved silently toward the place where the birds had gone. They pushed their way through young bamboo slender as fishing rods, growing so closely that it rose like a springy fence; beyond was a small glade, beyond that was lantana, the edge of the true jungle.

After moving a few yards they stood up, disappointed that the peacocks were not there and had gone deeper into the dark jungle. Ramlal, searching the glade carefully, stiffened. He touched his son's shoulder and pointed.

Thirty yards away on the forest edge, rising straight up

from its coil, its hood spread, was a black cobra. One third of the deadly snake's five-foot length was in the air, swaying as gently as a leaf in a breeze. The hard eyes were fixed on something in the grass before it.

Frightened by the snake, which was now beginning to move its head from side to side, they backed away. The cobra flicked its head toward them. It stopped swaying and fixed them in its stone-cruel gaze.

In some parts of India people believe in *nagula panchami,* cobra worship. They bow and pray before the snakes, feed them live animals and birds, and protect them from those who would kill them. I saw a young man in a village near Mysore each morning bring a dish of milk to a black cobra that lived in a stone wall near an abandoned temple. It was a chilling sight, the man placing the milk, waiting while the snake wiggled from the rocks. The result of this superstitious worship often is death for the cultist. Although the government has often cautioned the people and even tried to dissolve the cult of the cobra, the strange religion continues.

Here in the central region the cobra is feared as the jungle's worst killer. In a census taken one year it was discovered that twenty thousand forest people had been killed by the snake. *Naja maja tripudians,* the common Indian cobra, has twin poison fangs fixed in the front of its upper jaw, and kills by striking forward and biting. The venom acts directly on the nervous system in an action so rapid that it often brings death within minutes.

These jungles also hold the king cobra, or hamadryad, which grows to a length of twelve feet, a monster whose bite almost always causes sudden death, and the spitting cobra, or ringhals. Its poison, which can permanently blind a person, is effectively thrown six feet or more.

This one threatening Ramlal and Sammar was the common cobra, like the one Kipling's mongoose had fought and killed. As the jungle people know, when its hood is spread it is annoyed, ready to strike anything that gets in its way. The hood is formed by the agitated snake lifting and pushing forward its upper ribs, the skin then stretching over the cage that is formed.

Now, as Ramlal and Sammar backed away, perhaps hoping to turn and run before the snake started for them, the cobra dropped to the ground. Man and boy gripped their axes and waited. But the snake suddenly whipped around. They could see it slithering off into the jungle growth.

Twenty feet from where the cobra had lifted its painted head (the back of the hood looking as if the snake were wearing white spectacles), the grass moved and something scurried toward them. It was less than half the size of a cat; its fur was a sprinkle of black and gray, and it moved as gracefully as a flow of water. It was a young mongoose, called *newara* in Central India.

With a quick sweep of his right hand Ramlal tossed his net, imprisoning it. It struggled in the mesh briefly, then lay motionless, looking up at the man and the boy.

Ramlal didn't have to explain that they had happened upon a not unusual situation. The cobra was waiting to strike the mongoose, timing it carefully, for the snake was aware that if it missed it would immediately have the mongoose's teeth in its neck. The peacock hunters had distracted the snake, and probably saved the mongoose's life. Despite Kipling, it is rare that an immature animal wins the battle with an adult cobra.

As they walked along the road to the village, the boy carrying the mongoose in the net, we can imagine his father telling him some of the facts about mongooses that he had learned in his forty-five years of living in the jungle.

"Newara," he might have said, "live in holes in the ground that they dig." Then pointing to the netted animal his son was carrying, he asked, "See his claws on the front feet? He can dig a hole faster than I can with both hands and a stick. No other has ears like him. Fold after fold.

He can close each fold so that nothing enters his ears when he goes into a hole to catch a snake or a rat, or when he builds his house in the earth.

"He hunts only in the day, and is so brave and strong that he doesn't hunt like the panther or the tiger. He doesn't hide and creep out to attack his enemies. He rushes like the bull buffalo. But newara is clever. He likes meat, but when he cannot get it he will eat fruit and our vegetables. I have even seen newara smash the shells of forest snails against rocks to get his meat.

"When the winds blow cold a coat grows under this black-and-gray fur, keeping him warmer than we in our Mulni huts. Newara has a family five times every year, with three children in each family. As they grow, the mother picks them up by the neck and moves them from burrow to burrow. She is very wise. She does this to confuse the enemies, the panther and the great birds of prey. She also protects them, even with her life. I have seen a grown newara drive off a jackal ten times her size.

"Newara often attacks others larger than himself. But his favorite prey is rats and mice, frogs and snakes. My father had a newara when I was a boy that kept our hut and the place near us free of all of these things, the scorpions that bite you and make you sick, the insects that make sleep poor.

"When the monsoon rains come and the snakes are brought out of their hiding places and into our fields and homes, newara comes and kills them. He is our friend. Often he will stay after the rains and protect us from rats and snakes and live with us.

"Newara is so fast that even the cobra is afraid of him. When the snake strikes and misses, newara flashes in and bites his head until the snake is dead. He can make his fur and his tail grow to twice its size. This can cause the cobra to fall short in his strike. Then he is a dead one.

"But the great cobras such as we just saw are often attacked by two newara. I saw it happen once. They ran around the snake, rushing in close to make it strike. When it struck and missed, both newara leaped as one. The great cobra thrashed and fought, curling and recurling its thick coils. But the newara hung on until it was dead."

Until this point in our speculation of what Ramlal may have told his son, the information is accurate. But now, as his voice undoubtedly took on the softer tone of awe, he began to tell Sammar about beliefs that scientists have discounted as folklore.

"Newara," he said, as the Gonds believe, "have a special magic that make them unlike the rest of us. The bite of the cobra doesn't harm them. If they are bitten in battle they find the root of the 'mangus wail.' They chew it and live.

They also have a patch on their tongues as sharp as our thorns that in its special way prevents the cobra poison from doing its fatal work."

Mongooses do have that patch, but it is rough papillae that aid them in licking meat from the bones of their prey.

As many an Indian boy before him, Sammar must have been elated at the prospect of keeping the interesting animal with him for a while. Having met several village boys like Sammar who had pet mongooses, I think I know what happened next.

The mongoose was kept in a wicker crate in the rear of the hut. Sammar fed him buffalo milk in a hollowed gourd, and probably insects and lizards that he caught. He must have kept the mongoose there for several days, until he thought that it was safe to let him out. When he did open the cage, the mongoose came out as if hurled. But, being young and liking people, probably full of food and feeling safe, he wouldn't immediately leave the hut. After investigating it, he would climb Sammar's shoulder, and, like many another mongoose has done to a friendly boy, peer into his face, and stick his pink nose into Sammar's ear until the boy giggled.

After making his appraisal of boy and hut he flashed out of the door in a movement so fast that it reminded Sammar of the streaks of silver made by darting *mahseer* fish in the Tawa. He would be gone for hours, and as mongooses are daylight hunters, would return at dusk, perhaps with a lizard. He would come back because his breed respond to the friendly company of small boys.

We can imagine what happened as the mongoose continued to stay in the hut, seemingly content, although his bright eyes took in every movement, from the stirrings of Sammar and Ramlal to the progress of a buffalo fly on the supposedly insectproof dung wall. He would leave the hut for an hour or so at a time, always for food, always returning. Nights as the samburs' pooking barks came across the valley, and the peacocks' cat cries sounded, Sammar might try to sleep with the mongoose on his chest, first for a half hour, then stretching the periods until they were sleeping companions.

The mongoose would be locked in his wicker cage during the day, while his young master was gone to guard the animals.

I have often walked back to a village at sundown along a jungle road with a herd boy like Sammar. As the pink clouds pale and the gray of the coming night seeps across the sky, the slabs of rock, inset like gems in the ring of earth beside the road, cast a greenish glow in the neardark. The night-jars flit in sudden bat flights, silent, ghostly birds of the dark that still startle although they are on the road every evening.

The summer days in the jungle are hot and still, the earth is so parched that it splits. Even the lizards pant on the walls of huts, tongues suspended like pieces of thread. Rain is always desperately needed. When it comes it brings a change in the villagers' lives.

The usual enameled blue sky was abruptly gone one day just after Sammar went to bring the goats and buffaloes to pasture closer to the village. The storm came as he was driving the animals up the road, nudging laggards with his bamboo staff, the white dust spiraling, coating his face and bare legs and chest. It began as a light, tapping rain which freckled the dust on his cheeks. Then suddenly it came in a fire-hose drive that sent Sammar and his charges running. In seconds the drops became hail stones twice the size of marbles. Pelted, stinging from the sharp ice, Sammar drove the animals to a fenced pasture and then fled inside his hut.

Hail is not uncommon in the jungles at this time of year and often lasts for a half hour. Sammar sat on the dirt floor with the mongoose on his lap, listening until the rain again began a soft fall. Still holding the mongoose, he stepped outside.

After these sudden storms ice lays on the ground often two inches thick, and through the light rain the sun turns it into a flashing blue fire that twinkles and burns and winks like ten thousand diamond eyes.

The sight held Sammar in awe as it does everyone who sees it. Sammar bent and picked up a hail stone and placed it in his mouth, sucking it, drawing it in and out as the children do *patti,* the sugar and nut candy sold at village celebrations. All mongooses being curious, this one probably crawled up Sammar's chest, watching the ice in his mouth until he could stand the mystery of it no longer. He reached up and grabbed, the coldness of the bright object surprising him so that he spit it on the ground, chittering in reproach. Sammar laughed and returned to the hut as the pour of rain increased.

Ramlal must have gone about his daily chores much as usual, helping to cut bamboo for the forest contractor, tending his animals, keeping his eye on the gram fields, which were being beaten into mud by the heavy week-long rain. Sammar would have been told to stay in the hut, out of the wet. During these days he and the mongoose must have become even closer friends.

Then, one day, just as suddenly as it began, the hard rain stopped, the sun rose, the wind blew the clouds in wavy white lines, and fresh smells came from the jungle like perfume from a bottle.

That first cry often comes as a shrill *ki-ki-ki-ki-ki-ki-kee,*

starting as a short sound, rising in a crescendo, and ending in a scream. The cry of a striking bird of prey, the natural enemy of all mongooses. The furious barking of the dogs brought Sammar on the run. On his back, fighting for his life, the mongoose, like many another before him, was in the process of being lifted into the air by a *shah baz,* a crested hawk eagle, a fiercely beautiful white-and-brown spotted bird that lives on jungle fowl, pheasants, partridges, rabbits, and other small animals. Our mongoose was the right size for the hawk eagle, but he had more fight in him than the bird with its fearsome beak and talons had expected. That courage and the bark of the dogs saved his life.

Without hesitation Sammar rushed the bird, clubbing it off with his bamboo staff. Finally, rising straight up, the hawk left in a shower of feathers. Shaken and somewhat bloody, but unbowed, the mongoose bounced to his feet and sat upright, watching the shah baz gain altitude until it became a speck in the sky.

The end of the rainy season brought another change to the village. It came in the person of one of the forest contractors. They are a breed unto themselves, compounded of avarice and cunning. Anyone who has been in India's jungles long enough to become acquainted with them must have met a man like Laxman.

Born among the boiling mobs of Calcutta, he was not a kindly man, but he was a shrewd one. His intelligence and personality had been honed into predatory sharpness by the brutal poverty of that city. He had come first to the jungles as a two-rupee-a-day bamboo cutter, cheerfully enduring the labor to escape the clutch of Calcutta. It hadn't taken him long to advance, step by step, until now he was the one who decided where and when the bamboo would be cut, and was in a position to make many extra rupees from the forest people, buying and selling for a large profit anything they offered.

A fat man, dark with an oily skin, he was always perspiring. He looked as if he had been blown into his clothing as wheat is blown into bags. His flesh sagged from his frame, hung from his belly in folds. He always wore a soiled *dhoti* (a length of white cloth tied around the waist and hitched up between the legs) and a Bengali shirt (exceptionally long tails worn on the outside). Carrying a black umbrella that he used as a symbol of office, he aimed it furled at people to make his point. Unfurled he lofted it above his head as if he were being carried along in a palanquin, a servant protecting him from the sun with the black shield. He carried the impression off so well that as he walked it did seem that some force other than Laxman was holding the umbrella above his haughty head.

He also always wore a pair of black oxford-type shoes without stockings. It was his pride to keep them shining despite the dusty roads. In a region of barefoot people he knew that this was something else that set him apart, and he would often halt a conversation to take a cloth from his shirt pocket, bend over, and vigorously polish his shoes. Then rising back to his full height, he would pause and say, "Well?" in a tone of injured patience, as if the villagers had been purposely trying to keep him from an important task.

Laxman had learned early that people, especially those in the jungle, respect authority. He never talked; he commanded. His favorite words were, "It is not possible!" Since he was the one representative from the outside world the Gonds saw regularly, it made them almost happy with their lot, glad that they didn't move in a world peopled by Laxmans.

He would come to Mulni in a well-kept 1927 Model A Ford, announcing his arrival many times with the rubber-bulb horn that reminded the village boys of a lost buffalo calf bleating for its mother.

The Model A was Laxman's chariot. He alighted from it like Roman royalty come to inspect slaves. He took the high-chassied car in amazing places, over trails where the Gonds walked, up steep hills, across muddy roads. This re-

sult of the mechanical genius of Henry Ford enabled him
to know nearly every inch of the country. Its bamboo was
as familiar to him as the huts of Mulni. He knew when the
ringal would be ready for cutting, knew how much should
be cut in what length of time. He paid the villagers poorly
and always expected more work than they could possibly
produce. When the bamboo was down he would send
trucks out from Itarsi to gather it. On the return these
trucks also brought his loot.

This booty usually consisted of live animals or birds,
snakes or skins. In positions of supreme authority, forest
contractors have the opportunity to strike hard bargains
with the aboriginals. Their profit comes from sales to animal dealers, museum and zoo directors, who know that
the contractors often return from the jungle with excellent
specimens. A peacock bought for six rupees can bring
twenty or even more; a young leopard can net as much as
one hundred dollars. But no sale is too small for a forest
contractor.

So after the rains Laxman came tooting his frog horn,
alighting, umbrella in hand, scorn on his heavy features.
We can well imagine the first words he said to the *gaon,*
the headman of Mulni. "It is not possible that you have
done such little work in all these days!"

As the headman protested that the rains had made it impossible to work as efficiently as usual, Laxman no doubt ignored him, held out a fat hand, and carefully inspected his fingernails.

When the headman had finished, he said sharply, "It is not possible!" and lifting the umbrella over his head, strode off, the headman and elders of Mulni trailing. He would go to the dak bungalow on the knoll overlooking the village. There he would sit on a wicker plantation chair with long arms that reached out so far they made it resemble a throne holding everyone at a respectful distance. As forest contractors do, he would tell each man how many rupees he had earned, lecture all of them on the need to work longer and harder, and ask what things they might have for sale. Even this he did in a typically devious way.

"What may Laxman do for the people of Mulni?" he would say. "What worthless things do you want me to take off this time?"

Then came the parade of people with unusual, often pitiful things to sell: a young civet cat, a baby leopard, two proud old peacocks, three half-grown cobras, a pangolin (a miniature scaly anteater), a tiny, recently weaned mouse deer, a giant red squirrel. One old man might even try to sell a gerbille.

At this Laxman would shake his head angrily. "A rat!

Old man, don't play these games with Laxman!" Then, taking in every face before him, he would ask, "Anything else?" If there was no response, he would count out a few rupees to pay for the animals, and give instructions as to how they were to be crated.

Then again, "Anything else?"

This time the headman spoke timidly, afraid not to tell the truth. "Ramlal has a newara."

Ramlal scowled at him. "It is not for sale. It belongs to my son."

"A newara, a mungoose, eh?" Laxman put this information into his mind and let it rotate for several moments to see what would develop. One could always sell a mungoose to the snake charmers in Madras. He asked, "Anyone else have a mungoose?"

There was a shaking of heads.

"Ramlal," Laxman said carefully, "I think I would like that mungoose and any more you can get in the future."

Ramlal stubbornly shook his head. "It is not mine to sell. It is Sammar's."

"A boy," Laxman scoffed. "He is yours to command."

Ramlal shook his head again.

Everyone was watching. Laxman knew that now the situation involved more than just getting the mungoose. His authority was being challenged. If he is to keep a village under his thumb, a forest contractor cannot allow this to happen. The thrall would begin to slip if a man like Ramlal could successfully defy him.

"I think," he said slowly, "that if Ramlal does not sell Laxman his mungoose then Ramlal will never sell Laxman anything else. Even his labor."

Ramlal knew that he couldn't let this happen. To make an enemy of a man like Laxman was to drive yourself from your village. Finally he said, "I will get the newara."

Laxman waved his hand nonchalantly. "The trucks will be here in two days. Place it in a wicker cage. See that it is on the Kesla-Bori road, one mile from here, at three o'clock that afternoon."

Ramlal nodded and left. He wanted to tell his son before anyone else in the village did. It would not be easy.

We can imagine the scene, Sammar listening intently as Ramlal tried to explain: "And if we do not sell your newara, Laxman can make trouble. He must always have what he asks for."

"Not this time!" Sammar said fiercely. "I will take my newara and leave Mulni!"

"It wouldn't help," Ramlal replied. "The trouble would follow. We can always get another newara. There are many in the jungle."

Sammar, who had been taught to think like a man, now had to act like one.

"There aren't any more like mine," he said slowly. "I

will never forget him. Take him now, Father. I don't want
to be here when the trucks come."

This is how the mongoose could have left his jungle, in
a wicker cage, in a rickety truck with pink-and-blue murals
of mountains and a river painted on its doors by the driver,
a truck that backfired often and bounced at every bump.

It is listed in shipping registry records that the British
freighter *Athel Prince* came into harbor at Madras, on the
southeast coast of India, during the summer of 1962. She
came past the catamarans and the surf boats, still stitched
together with leather thongs, as they have been for hundreds of years, and the big dhowlike boats with faded sails
bellying in the offshore breeze, past the motored craft from
Europe that rode low in the swell, unloading machinery,
grain, hardware, sugar, asphalt, canned goods, and refilling
their holds with silk, brass, hides, bright cottons, and un-
processed tobacco.

The *Athel Prince* is a freighter converted from a World
War II American Liberty ship. Sea-soiled, a bit rusty, her
sides scabrous with patches of ocean slime, she rattled as
she came into port. Before she was completely unloaded,
seamen anxious for shore leave rushed off like fleas leaving an old dog entering water. Madras is a favorite port
for merchant seamen, with fascinating bazaars and shops

jammed to the ceilings, overflowing to the sidewalks with mystic Oriental wares, everything from carved *hookahs*, water pipes smoked from three-foot holders, to gleaming hand-beaten brass tables, tiger-claw brooches polished so the bone shone like finest ivory, and filmy multicolored silk saris for the girls back home.

It is the schooling center of the art of the dance, with many outdoor recitals to which the public is invited, to see the graceful, strikingly beautiful girls perform. It is the second film city, and movie actors and actresses and crews are always at work on sets that duplicate everything from palaces out of the Mogul past to a cunningly designed battle scene.

One sailor from the *Athel Prince* (we know that he is English, an ordinary seaman in his twenties) made his way to Binny's Road from the Connemara Hotel, where he had probably stopped and had a cup of tea. There is action on Binny's Road, the snake charmers are there, hawk-faced men with ten-year-old boy apprentices, and street merchants whose spread blankets are covered with the brassware and paste jewelry they hope to sell, turbaned boys selling sugar cane juice pressed through dirty hand rollers, sometimes a skinny man wrestling a sad, toothless old bear on a chain. It is a good location, near the Connemara Hotel, where many tourists stop, running into a main artery,

Commander-in-Chief Road, which carries much of Madras' traffic. The snake charmers are the main attraction. When the crowds are large enough, they entice the cobras from baskets with flutes and yank the mongooses on cords and the fight is on. Mongoose darting in, snake striking.

I have watched it often, and can picture the scene now as the sailor must have seen it, walking up Binny's Road:

Indians are gathered before two sitting men, one young, the other old, with a gun-metal beard; both have dirty gray turbans, the old man has long, once-white pantaloons, the younger one a dhoti. Two round baskets are before them; several feet from the baskets are two mongooses, cords around their necks tied to two wooden pegs that have been driven into the ground.

The audience is made up mostly of Indians in turbans and dhotis, men in fancy vests and wide, flapping white trousers; women in a rainbow of saris, children wearing gaily striped long-tailed shirts and little else.

As the young man behind the basket begins to play a fat-bellied flute, a snake head dances out of each basket. Then the cobras come most of the way out, seemingly lured by the music, and sway back and forth. Many scientists agree that snakes are deaf, and that the flute is just dramatic window dressing. The swaying, they claim, is actually an imitation of the movement of the man before them.

Now, as the sailor watches, the old snake charmer twitches the cord on the larger mongoose and tips the snake basket. The black cobra comes out in a coil, then rises, its hood extended. The mongoose, prodded by a long bamboo stick, scoots forward. The snake lances out, missing the mongoose by a foot, recoils as the mongoose circles in a whirling, dancelike movement. As the cobra strikes again and lays stretched out as it misses, the mongoose, fast as the flick of a whip, has the snake by the throat. The boy toots his flute until it screams, the old man runs around with a basket, hoping to fill it with rupees, as the cobra writhes and the mongoose battles.

When he sees that he isn't going to fill the basket, the old man dashes back to the cobra, lifts it by the tail, and cruelly jerks the cord tied to the mongoose, spilling it in the dust.

Although most of the spectators, even the Indians, don't realize it, the cobras have had their fangs removed and are harmless. But the mongooses, no matter how long they have played this street game, are serious. They will kill the cobras if they can, and this is the reason they are tied and jerked back when they seem to be winning. The charmers can't afford to buy new snakes after each performance.

The sympathies of the crowd are always with the mongooses. It is sad the way they are handled. Perhaps that is why the sailor bought his mongoose—to take him out of his bondage to the old snake charmer. I know that I myself bought a mongoose for that reason, but wasn't permitted to put it aboard my plane.

If you buy anything in the East you must bargain for it. It is a way of life and is expected. Having gone through the same thing, I can imagine the haggle the sailor faced.

"Sell that skinny little mongoose that looks like a starved monkey?" he began.

The snake charmer shook his head and said softly. "Not for sale."

The boy with the flute assisted. "No! He is a new one. We hope to make him the best snake fighter in Madras."

"Just the point," the sailor argued. "He's uneducated. I'd like to take him off your hands before you spend all that time on him. You have a good fighter in the other big chap. Seems a waste of money and food to keep two."

As both charmers shook their heads, the sailor saw a gleam beginning in the faded eyes of the old man.

"Two rupees," he said. "You can always get another—"

"No!" said the old beard. "He can make that in one fight."

"Maybe he won't fight. He's a young one," the sailor bargained.

Suddenly the old man said, "Thirty rupees."

The boy beside him screamed, "No! No! Not half enough!"

And so the bargaining went back and forth, until the old man finally pulled his beard, closed his eyes, and with a reluctant sigh said, "We cannot sit all day in the sun. Take him for twenty rupees."

# PART II

## The City

No ONE CAN SAY IT DID NOT HAPPEN THAT WAY. IT has before, and it will again. But what now follows is not based simply on a knowledge of the Indian jungle, its people and the typical ways of a mongoose. It actually happened. It is as true and as accurate as the memories of those involved can make it.

The destination of the *Athel Prince* after it had unloaded at Madras was Duluth, Minnesota, on Lake Superior.

During the first few days at sea the mongoose stayed in the sailor's duffel, on his bunk, but gradually he became used to the sea roll and the thump of the ship's motor. The sailor fed him milk and table scraps and occasionally a piece of raw meat, which he got from the cook in the galley. A few days at sea was enough to give the mongoose the run of the ship. The crew became accustomed to the small gray animal following the sailor about as he did his work. He either trailed his new master like a dog, rode his shoulder, or crawled inside his shirt, napping while his owner swabbed the deck, helped clean the hold, or performed the other manual duties of the ordinary seaman.

As this was an English ship, there were two daily breaks in work routine for tea, midmorning and afternoon. The English like their tea strong, with plenty of milk and sugar, and the brewing, the steeping, the drinking are a ritual. The mongoose watched as the crew gathered, sipping tea and talking; often he was only inches from his sailor's cup.

One day he could resist it no longer: as the sailor sipped tea, he found that the mongoose's head was crowding him. At first, while the sailors watched in delight, the mongoose was overcautious with the steaming liquid, gingerly testing it with a paw, but as he was encouraged he lapped and liked the hot, sugary liquid and soon had his own cup set on the deck, where he could handle it any way he wanted. From that point on he was a tea-drinking mongoose who looked for his cup at teatime.

He quickly became the ship's mascot. He liked to untie shoes, hide in boxes and suddenly pop his head out, go to the galley and sit, tail back, and beg raw meat from the cook. He also liked to lie on his back, feet waving, and wrestle.

So, knowing mongooses with their charm and friendliness, I think those days aboard the *Athel Prince* as she

made her way across the choppy Atlantic must have brought the animal and the sailor into close and warm companionship.

But after two weeks at sea an incident caused the sailor to curtail his mongoose's activities. Of several other pets aboard picked up in various ports by crew members, the most conspicuous—next to the mongoose—was a gray monkey. Supposed to be a rhesus, a small species, it grew larger every day. Active, at times when its ramblings and curiosity were restrained, it became fierce.

The climax came one day when the five-foot cook looked up from stirring a pot of stew in the galley, to find the monkey staring at him at almost eye level.

He fled in protest to the captain, swearing that the beast had been about to brain him with a kettle.

So one evening when the ship sighted the Rock of Gibraltar rising from the mists, the captain decided that the monkey, now three times the size it was supposed to be when adult, must go. Its owner was distressed, but the order had to be obeyed. The problem: no one aboard, including the captain, wanted to give the animal the deep six. The ship's carpenter finally came up with the answer. He built a raft, the cook provided three days' provisions, and the monkey's owner found an oar.

The next morning the *Athel Prince* slowed her engine,

the raft was launched, and the monkey (probably a langur) was placed aboard. The whole crew gathered to say farewell as the raft with its gibbering passenger headed for Gibraltar. As it was just a few miles away and the wind was right, it is very likely that the famous apes of the Rock have an aggressive new personality in their midst today.

Bad news about his pet came to the sailor soon after his ship left the Atlantic and made port at Montreal, the first stop before they began the cruise inland along the St. Lawrence Seaway. Customs at Montreal, noticing the mongoose, told the sailor that he would run into difficulty, if he was seen with him in the United States.

After clearing Montreal the *Athel Prince* moved along one of the most interesting waterways in the world to Duluth, 2,342 miles from the sea.

It isn't known why the sailor waited until he arrived at Duluth to put the mongoose off the ship. He could have sold the animal or given it away at any one of many places on the Great Lakes-St. Lawrence Seaway system, which extends 2,150 miles from Cape Gaspe, on the Gulf of St. Lawrence, to the headwaters of the St. Louis River, in Minnesota. The *Athel Prince* moved from Lake Ontario along the Niagara River via the Welland Canal into Lake Erie, up the Detroit River to Lake St. Clair and the St. Clair

River to Lake Huron, then to St. Mary's River along the Sault Ste. Marie canals to Lake Superior.

Perhaps a decision was delayed because of the sailor's fascination with a first trip to the "Eighth Sea," as the Great Lakes with their water surface of 95,000 square miles and 8,300-mile coast line are called by seafarers. Even the old salts who have traveled it many times look forward to this system of lateral canals and locks that lift the ships in elevations from sea level in five stages. From the Atlantic Ocean along the thousand miles of the St. Lawrence River to Montreal the rise is 20 feet; then the ships actually sail 225 feet upward from Montreal to Lake Ontario; another 326 feet up to Lake Erie, 8 feet more into Lake Huron, and another 22 feet to Lake Superior and Duluth, until they have ascended a total of 601 feet.

The people at the Duluth Zoo who met the sailor believe that he was so close to his pet that he waited until the last minute to part with him, then did it in the most humane way he could.

He may even have heard about Duluth, its zoo, and the sort of place it was from other seamen who had been to this Nordic city on the western tip of Lake Superior. However he made his choice, it was a fortunate one. It is a warmhearted place where people smile at strangers.

Many are foreign-born and work or have worked in the

Mesabi, Coyuna, and Vermilion mines north of the city, once the nation's greatest source of iron ore. They have kept an old world love of order, and their small frame houses that make up the majority of hillside homes, many weathered gray as driftwood by storm and wind, have those European, almost geometrically precise squares of lawn, flower and vegetable gardens. Nearly every yard has a lilac bush. In June, when the fragrant purple flowers hang heavy and the winds blow from the great inland sea and a mistlike rain falls, the scent gathers from the thousands of wet lilacs, lifts, and is wafted away in a sweet perfume that is a nostalgic, unforgettable mark of the city.

Climatically not unlike Norway (Mark Twain quipped that the coldest winter he had ever spent was a summer in Duluth), this city of more than a hundred thousand has attracted many foreign-born Scandinavians, twenty-thousand of them Finns, at least 30 percent from the Nordic countries—rugged people who ignore weather and hardships and are fighters for a cause.

An incident in the early history of Duluth points up the character of its people. Needing a canal through Minnesota Point to the harbor, they started to dig one despite the protests of Superior (in Wisconsin, on the other side of the harbor), which feared a loss of revenue, as the existence of a Duluth canal would mean that all ships would then not have to use the Superior harbor entry. In a swift political move, Superior managed to get an injunction halting progress on the canal.

A telegram arrived in Duluth on Saturday, stating that Congress had issued an injunction to stop the canal work. To make things worse, the dredge that had been working overtime struck frozen gravel. Knowing that the injunction would be delivered on Monday morning, most of Duluth's able-bodied citizens who could wield a shovel or pick or could tote a basket or bucket showed up at the point and worked until the canal was finished.

While the injunction papers were on the way, all through Saturday and Sunday the people worked; the women kept fires going, rushing hot coffee and food to the workers. On Sunday, Superior residents rowed boats over to watch and jeer.

At dawn on Monday, Captain Sherwood ran his small steam yacht *Frank C. Fero* from the lake through the new canal into the bay, its whistle screaming. As he wheeled the yacht around to take her through again, the army engineer arrived with the injunction. By then the canal was fifty feet wide, running eight feet of water.

From that small canal dug by the people Duluth has become, combined with Superior, one of the most important ports in the United States, her record of daily arrivals and departures standing at ninety-four ships, her top yearly tonnage 77,243,545 short tons. From a single canal and a breakwater the harbor has grown into a frontage of forty-nine miles of dredged canals with seventy-one wharves for general freight, six for iron ore, twelve coal docks, and twelve grain elevators.

Of the 235 ships that sailed into Duluth-Superior Harbor in 1959, when the Seaway opened, the British *Ramon DeLarrinaga* was the first deep-draft vessel to arrive.

The *Athel Prince* came into this harbor in light ballast late on September 9, 1962. It had been misty and overcast from the moment she entered Lake Superior, the world's largest body of fresh water which is 383 miles long and has a water surface of 31,820 square miles—water that could be as violent and unpredictable as any ocean.

The trip to the harbor was rough, the weather giving a foretaste of what was to come in a few months, when it could start to ice and the winds could become so strong that few vessels would try to battle them. This foretaste was fog, beginning in a haze as light as cigarette smoke, rapidly becoming so heavy that the foghorn at Duluth South Breakwater Light Station, which operated at only zero to five miles' visibility, began its grunting like a great animal in pain—the hoarse sound audible for twelve miles. Blasting every minute in one long, continuous sound, then in a sharper short sound the second time around, it brought the *Athel Prince* through the wool of fog and the dark of predawn.

As she crept her way carefully, it began to rain, a southeast wind sprang up, and visibility was reduced to one eighth of a mile. It was unfortunate for many of the first-timers of the crew that she arrived in this weather at this hour, for it is an inspiring sight, Duluth suddenly rearing up out of her sea, rising to twelve hundred feet at points along the outcropping of ancient volcanic gabbro rock.

It was too dark and foggy even to see the 21-million-dollar tracery of the Hi-Bridge throw light in flaming spears into the water; so blanked out that no one saw the warm welcoming ring of harbor lights as the old sea-beaten Liberty ship, guided by foghorn and radio, finally came into the basin and made her way slowly up the narrow slip of dark water to moor beside Cargill Grain Elevators.

It had been a long, hard, sometimes perilous journey from Madras on its green tip beside the Bay of Bengal. The mongoose was many miles from his jungle.

At ten o'clock on the morning of September 10 the sound of the phone came clacking through the door left ajar in the preparation room of the Duluth Zoo, its insistent mechanical call rising even above the rumble of the lions. The first to hear it was Lloyd Hackl, the director, carefully watching a jaguar to detect if a limp that had been reported by one of the caretakers was pronounced enough to require a veterinarian's examination. As usual, he hurried to answer the phone. Lloyd Hackl remembers the conversation going like this.

"This is a seaman at the piers. I've got a nice mongoose chap that I'd like to sell. Is your zoo interested?"

"We're interested," said the director, "but we don't have funds for this sort of thing. We can buy animals only after our directors have met and approved. I'm sorry."

There was a long silence. Then, "Would you come and pick 'im up and take good care of the little chap if I gave 'im to you?"

"We would," Lloyd Hackl replied. "And I thank you. We don't have a mongoose. And, incidentally, we take good care of *all* our animals."

"I've heard," the seaman said. "We're at Cargill Elevators. Could you send someone along?"

Hackl said that he would, and hung up. He found John Mealey, a short, crew-cut, arm-tattooed man in his fifties, hand-brushing the slate-gray hide of the Indian elephant, Bessie, his charge. The elephant had her trunk curled, muttering in delight.

"John," Hackl said, "we've just got an offer of a mongoose. Will you and Bob Stevenson take the truck and get it?"

In the zoo's 1956 Ford pickup they drove east for three miles, then south on Route 53, turning off at 400 Garfield Avenue and up the long gravel road to the slip of water beside Cargill Grain Elevators.

It was after the lunch hour, and activity had resumed along the pier: the seven great gray cylinders nearest the slip hung orange spouts like umbilical cords into the hold of a ship, and Mealey and Stevenson could hear the swish of grain sweeping through them. Beside the grain elevators stood two tremendous dull gray warehouses connected by a hundred-yard aluminum chute. Across the mooring slip two giant cranes stood like prehistoric birds pecking at anthills of coal.

The ship herself, peeling, sea-weathered Gothic letters naming her *Athel Prince,* creaked in the soft slap of the slip, and Mealey, an ex-bosun's mate with eleven years of naval duty, said to Stevenson, "God help 'em! A Liberty ship! I'd sooner cross in a Chris-Craft!"

As they came closer, carrying the crate into which they were going to put the mongoose, they saw two young men in heavy sweaters and trousers, both with beards, one dark, one blond.

"You Yanks from the zoo?" the dark one asked.

"Yes," said Mealey. "You the one called about giving us a mongoose?"

The dark youth nodded. "And you don't need a cage. This mongoose is people-broke." He pulled up his sweater. Out poked a furry head.

The seaman reached in and, gently pulling him out, placed the mongoose on Mealey's shoulder. Although accustomed to animals, Mealey, not sure what this was, appeared uneasy.

The seamen laughed; the dark one said, "He's been riding my shoulder or sleeping in my shirt all the way from India. Don't worry about 'im. He's tame. He likes raw meat best, but will eat vegetables, even cooked cereal."

"And tea," the blond boy said. "He likes hot tea in a cup with milk and sugar. He takes it with us every day."

"Right, Yanks," the dark seaman said, coming over and running his hand gently over the mongoose's head, the animal lifting it into the petting. "Take good care of 'im. He's come a long way."

He was silent for a moment, then he said to the mongoose, "Good-bye, chap. You've had a hard time, but maybe this is the place where you start to get the breaks."

Then he turned abruptly and walked off, up the concrete apron of the pier toward the road, the blond seaman following.

Mealey and Stevenson stood watching them go, listening to the wheat singing through the chutes, then Mealey gave the mongoose to Stevenson and they got into the truck. In seconds the animal was under Stevenson's coat, but he kept his head out, watching the two men.

"Looks like a cross between an otter and a squirrel," said Mealey.

"And a real pet. He's not a bit afraid," Stevenson added.

"The kids'll love him."

"Sure will," said Stevenson, "but you know what, Johnny, we forgot to ask his name. A pet like this must have a name."

"You're right," said Mealey as he drove out to Garfield Avenue and turned right, moving north, "but they seemed in a hurry to get away. Wonder why."

"Probably sentiment. You know how people get tied up with animals. Look at you and that elephant."

Mealey laughed. "I think I'm going to get tied up with this fella, too. Look!"

The mongoose was pulling pencils out of his coat pocket, stopping occasionally to examine the erasers. When Stevenson pushed the pencils back, the mongoose leaped to his shoulder, chittering like a squirrel.

They were silent as they drove under the trestle that crossed Oneonta Street; a string of small metal dump cars humped with red iron ore clattered over their heads across the tracks toward the railroad yard beyond.

"You know that TV comic strip character?" Mealey said suddenly. "The serious little guy that makes you laugh? Mr. Magoo? Why don't we call him Magoo?"

As the mongoose snuggled under his coat again, Stevenson said, "A natural! Hey, Magoo!" The animal stuck his head out. "Johnny, I've got to give you credit. I like it. Rhymes. Magoo. Zoo. Hey, Mr. Magoo, welcome to our zoo."

The Duluth Zoo, off Highway 23 at the western end, six miles from the center of the city, at 7210 Fremont Street, is a two-story, white-front brick building on the outside edge of seven acres, with a golden lion sitting on each side of the entrance. One hundred yards to the right a black Northern Pacific Railroad engine stands on silent exhibit; several feet to the left are two half-grown elms and a birch, its bark as white as a snowdrift. Before the zoo is the usual park with the out-of-tune carousel, the tricky rides, the refreshment stand. On summer days the laughter of children can be heard above the music.

The lions, long a landmark of Duluth, were brought to the zoo in the twenties, when the Lyceum Theater was remodeled and the golden cats that had graced the theater entrance for years were thought to be out of harmony. Al Anson, the theater manager, didn't want to junk them, so he telephoned and said that he had a pair of lions he would like to donate if the zoo would pay for transportation. Enthused, the zoo officials accepted, and purchased great quantities of raw meat for the cats. These were their first really important animals, and the director and caretakers waited in front of the zoo for the truck to arrive with the African lions. There is no record of their verbal reaction when the two wooden figures were deposited at their door, but it was said that the theater manager was an unwelcome visitor at the Duluth Zoo for many months.

The zoo itself came into being when the Pittsburgh Steel and Wire Company wrote the city and asked that it return a quantity of wire. The steel company had donated the wire to Duluth with the understanding that it would be used to construct a zoo. This had not been done, so they wanted the wire. The city commissioners, reluctant to return any gift to the city, immediately pushed plans for a zoo.

They discovered that a printer, Bert Onsgard, had a fawn, "Rainbow," apparently a friendly little creature. On the basis of this and the strength of the supposition that Onsgard must be talented with wild creatures, the Duluth Business Men's Club made him chairman in charge of obtaining animals. The *Herald* stated, "Any citizens having mountain lions or other pets they would like to give the zoo, see the city commissioners."

From this unprofessional beginning in 1923, the Duluth Zoo has grown into a remarkably large and complete one for a city of its size.

Now this September afternoon as Mealey and Stevenson drove in with the mongoose, the usual too-early winter sun was washing over the gilt lions and the park was still. The only sound as they stopped the truck came from a dinner bell atop the zoo roof tolled at three thirty (feeding time) by head zookeeper Bruer Hage. It rang as clear as a carillon, and although it had no true tune or melody, its significant Pavlovian sound sang out daily, bringing every man and beast in the zoo alert. As the two men entered, the animals were restlessly pacing in their cages.

Directly facing the entrance was the bank of monkey cages, where the animals sat scratching, some apparently searching for fleas on one another in what actually is an act of status, of grooming, the big males getting the most attention. More curious about the spectators than the visitors are about them, the monkeys are the winners in this game of stare, peering, reaching man-hands through the bars, swinging and chattering. Now they were noisily awaiting food. An old man with a perplexed expression stood watching them.

Facing, as they went down one flight, with the mongoose still under Stevenson's coat, were the heavily barred cages of the lions, two tawny females and a maned male. Beside them a pair of Indian leopards, looking like giant

pieces of fireplace mantel porcelain come to life, were saw-
ing in anticipation, a coarse sound like that of wood being
cut with a ripsaw. Next to them a South American jaguar
padded up and down, blowing through his teeth in a noise
like that of gurgling water. All of the cats were in their
prime, hides polished by proper diet, unwinking eyes
gleaming like yellow topaz.

The sounds of a zoo just before feeding time rise into a
dreadful din, a cacophony that takes many a caretaker
months to learn to endure. The lions' shattering roars;
Bessie, the Indian elephant, trumpeting; Faru 11, the
rhino, snorting; the polar bears in a mighty thundering;
the gibbon apes, the squirrel monkeys, the dog-faced ba-
boons, and the whole variegated swarm of simians gibbering and shrieking in a nightmare of sound that subsides
into contented growlings and purrings and mumblings as
the caretakers drop chunks of raw meat into cages, dole out
bananas, ladle milk, or pass in vegetables.

"Why we put these cats right here, near the preparation room, gets me," Mealey said. "I been coming down
here for six years and they still stand my hair up."

They went past the rumbling of the big male lion into
the preparation room, where they knew the director would
be waiting.

The preparation room is dominated by a massive, waist-
high wooden chestlike table, projecting three feet from the

wall, occupying half of this area that is used for preparing special foods and examining the smaller animals. Often newcomers, if they aren't too large or too restless, are placed here to await housing space.

As Mealey and Stevenson entered they were carefully examined by two young barred owls standing on the table, fluffy gray birds with butter-yellow eyes, a pair that seemed in supreme command of the situation.

"Gift. Just arrived," Hackl said. "Did you get the mongoose?"

Lloyd Hackl, tall, with smooth, brushed-back silvering hair, heavy horn-bowed glasses that magnify a kindly expression, energetic and forceful at three years under the age most men retire, had no way of knowing that an historic meeting was about to take place.

The mongoose peeked out of Stevenson's coat.

Hackl laughed. "I wondered where the cage was. Friendly fellow, eh?"

"I'll say!" Mealey said. "He's a little beaut. Sticks with you like peanut butter."

"Johnny's got a great name for him, Mr. Hackl," Stevenson said. "Mr. Magoo."

"If it's okay with you," Mealey said.

"Sounds a good name," Hackl replied. "But let's take a look at this Mr. Magoo."

Stevenson reached in, got the mongoose, and placed him on his shoulder. Pink nose twitching, small ears moving, the animal took one sweeping look at the room, leaped on Hackl's shoulder, twittered as he saw the baby owls, sprang in a lightning movement to the table, and with short, aggressive steps stalked the birds.

The three men stood watching as the mongoose got within nose-touching distance of the owls, circled, came back to the edge of the table, and broad-jumped again to the zoo director's shoulder.

"These owls have upset him," Hackl said. "Look at the way he's puffed his fur. Makes him look twice as big. Even his tail seems doubled in size. This is quite a little fellow. I'm going to have to do some reading up on mongooses. Or is it mongeese?"

"Search me," Mealey answered.

As the director examined him carefully, Stevenson said, "Johnny thinks he looks like a cross between an otter and a squirrel."

"Not bad, John," Hackl said. "Narrow, tapering head, pinkish around face and chest, yellowish eyes, almost seal-brown feet, nonretractable claws. Look like good strong ones, five on each foot. Small, rounded ears with amazing fold construction."

He placed the mongoose on the table and examined his

teeth. "Forty, just like the civet. And this is a young one. Sound gums; firm, small teeth. Look at his black-and-white hair; the longer ones are marked with alternate dark and light rings which give him this speckled or salt-and-pepper look. I'd say he was about fifteen inches long, the tail maybe thirteen or fourteen."

"Way he lets you handle him," Mealey said, "I'd say he's about the tamest animal we got in the zoo."

As the zoo was quiet now at feeding time, Hackl was reminded of the problem of food. "What does he eat, did you find out?"

"Let me see," Mealey said. "The sailors were quick getting away from us, but they did say a couple things. Raw meat. Milk; vegetables, even cereal, I think. But I remember raw meat and milk."

"And hot tea with sugar," Stevenson said.

"Are you serious?" Hackl said.

"That's what they told us. Said he liked to take tea with them."

Stevenson went to get some milk with a raw egg beaten in, as suggested by Lloyd Hackl. The owls were taken into another room, and Mr. Magoo did a thorough job of investigation, poking in open boxes, prying in corners. He halted his detective work occasionally and sat up, tail back, to survey the situation.

"Like our kangaroo," Mealey said.

The mongoose sniffed at the dish of milk and egg when it arrived and drank all of it, lapping like a cat.

"Gentlemen," announced the director of the zoo, "I think we have a personality among us."

The next few days were to prove the observation an apt one. Mr. Magoo virtually took over the zoo.

The first step was location. The carpenter built a commodious cage, one side heavily wired so Mr. Magoo would be visible. He also built a smaller inside box, shaped like a house, with "Mr. Magoo" lettered in white.

It was decided to place him on the lower level, near the preparation room. A good decision, for Mr. Magoo spent more time with the caretakers in that room than he did in his cage.

Mealey soon discovered that Mr. Magoo liked to roll on his back and wrestle, wrapping his legs around Mealey's arm, rolling and growling, but never breaking the skin or using his teeth and claws. This bout went on nearly every day at the coffee hour—only now Mealey and even the director often changed the habit of years and drank tea.

It happened the third day, when Mealey, who had asked to be Mr. Magoo's caretaker, remembered that the mongoose was supposed to like tea. He got a cup, stirred in sugar and milk, placed it on the table in the preparation room, and put Mr. Magoo beside it.

He walked carefully around it, sniffed, went into his

kangaroo stance, then looked up at Mealey. But he didn't
drink the tea.

"What d'you suppose is wrong?" Mealey said to Stevenson, who was watching.

Stevenson shook his head, stood looking at Mr. Magoo,
then snapped his fingers. "Know what? I think you've got
to drink with him. Remember that blond limey said he
drank tea *with* them."

"No," Mealey said, "that couldn't be. If he likes tea, he
likes tea."

"I don't know," Stevenson replied, "animals are funny.
Bessie won't let anyone else feed her but you."

Reluctantly Mealey got a cup of tea, pushed Magoo's
nearer to him, and started sipping.

Mr. Magoo watched, then slowly began to sip the hot
tea, stopping occasionally to look up at Mealey and lick his
lips.

Mealey stared. "A tea-swizzling mongoose! Nobody'll
believe it!"

The next day the experiment was repeated, with Lloyd
Hackl observing. This went on for several days, until Mr.
Magoo finally learned to take tea solo, often in his cage.
Breaking the mongoose of the group habit came as the re-
sult of a remark by Mealey. One morning when mongoose
and men were drinking tea in the preparation room, Mea-

ley thought aloud that it would make quite a sight if the directors of the Arrowhead Society, sponsors of the zoo, should walk in. Shortly after that Magoo began to have tea alone.

Hackl and Mealey often took Mr. Magoo out into the sun for a walk past the bear pits and the elk enclosure. Mr. Magoo, free, frolicked in the grass like a puppy, but always responded to a whistle or a call when they started back to the main building.

"He's used to strolling with people," Mealey remarked during the first walk. "He was very close to someone, that's for sure."

Magoo was growing, filling out on a diet of raw horse meat steak, milk and eggs, tea, and sometimes raw vegetables. Taking to his zoo residence with remarkable aplomb, he began to sit up and protest in a loud chitter when his tea didn't arrive on time. Often after tea or a dinner steak he sprawled on his back, feet waving in the air in relaxed appreciation.

Mealey remembers seeing Magoo angry only once. A visitor had bought a souvenir toy green snake that wiggled realistically when held in the middle of the plastic body. He stopped beside the mongoose's cage, snake writhing in his hand. Magoo's eyes grew red. His hair bristled. He ran around his cage. As the visitor held the snake closer, Magoo sat up and yelped.

"I think he would have taken that toy snake, man's arm, and all," Mealey says. "He was mighty upset."

Although most zoogoers had no idea what a mongoose was, Mr. Magoo's personality soon made him one of the most popular animals. This was no small accomplishment, for he was surrounded by exotic and friendly animals. The familiar, friendly ones were beside him on the north wall: five guinea pigs, four chipmunks, four gray squirrels (both chipmunks and squirrels had treadmills, which they kept revolving, running rapidly inside them to keep them spinning); farther along were two South American large-billed toucans and three talking myna birds.

On the south wall were Valarie, the brown Himalayan bear, and Sheba, Cleo, and Nemo, the lions; beside them, Mike and Dagmar, the Indian leopards; next to them, the black leopards, Jake and Maggy; then the cages of Pete, the South American jaguar, and Johnny, the giant anteater.

Yet, even with all of this colorful competition, when the zoogoers had shivered beside the cats, ahed over the long-snouted anteater, clucked at the fat brown-and-white guinea pigs, watched with fascination as the squirrels and chipmunks tumbled in their treadmills, waited impatiently for the myna birds to say something interesting, they then stood before Mr. Magoo. He often sat up and stared back. If it was feeding time he would pause from his raw steak and chitter companionably at his guests.

During the next several weeks Lloyd Hackl and the zoo caretakers discovered what an unusual gift from the sea Mr. Magoo was. The director dug into books, read natural history articles, and called curators, picking brains for mongoose material.

He learned that the mongoose is the true Pied Piper, that in the late Eighties Jamaican planters had brought in several pairs to assist in waging what had been a losing war against the big cane rats that were threatening to destroy both sugar and rum industries. Ferrets, traps, poison, guns, even bounties had been tried. Nothing had stopped the plague.

But the mongooses did. In less than two years they had cleared the rats from the sugar cane fields. Today there are many mongooses in the West Indies and few rats, but Hackl discovered that far from being grateful to the animals for actually making the islands solvent again, many residents are complaining that they kill some game birds and beneficial snakes and lizards. Little mention is being made now of the thousands of dollars the mongooses saved by wiping out the rats.

Hackl also found that the mongoose's legendary snake-fighting ability is really a process of tiring the cobra with dancing and nimble side-stepping. While he engages the snake, the mongoose hums a song of battle, the sound not unlike a taut wire being vibrated. When the cobra tires from the constant striking and recoiling, the mongoose darts in and crushes the snake's skull. He has such powerful jaws that this is usually accomplished in a single bite. Hackl learned that if the mongoose was so disposed he could put his teeth completely through a man's hand in one swift motion, but that this seldom happened because of all the wild animals the mongoose is said to be among the friendliest to man.

In *Animal Facts and Fallacies,* by Osmond P. Breland, Hackl read that there were many superstitions and exaggerated claims regarding the mongoose's immunity from snake poison, and that, trying to gather facts, Clifford Pope of the Chicago Natural History Museum had watched a fight between a mongoose and a cobra. The mongoose was bitten near the mouth several times without any ill effect. But he never let the cobra bite any other part of his body. Pope thought there was something in the chemical make-up of the mongoose that served as protection in the area around the mouth, causing the poison to be absorbed so slowly that no harm resulted. He also believed that if the cobra had bitten the mongoose on the body or legs it probably would have died.

Zoo visitors also brought information. One day a sailor from an English freighter stood watching Mr. Magoo. John Mealey, ever trapped by the scent of salt water,

walked over to talk. He knew the man was off a ship without asking—the beard, the slight roll in the walk, the face burned browner than it could be by anything except a hard sun reflected from salt water.

"That's our mongoose," Mealey said. "From India. Some animal!"

"I know," the sailor said. "I've seen them in India. Eight months ago we had two do a job on our ship. This one brings it back."

"What d'you mean," Mealey said, "a job on your ship?"

"Quite a sight," the sailor said. "You been asea?"

"Bosun's mate. Eleven years on the salt."

"Then you know ships get rats and can't lose 'em?"

Mealey nodded.

The sailor laughed. "Well, one morning when we came into Bombay, there was this Indian at the dock, slat-thin, brown as a bean, dressed in those white diaper things that are tied around the waist and hitched up between the legs. He had two of these mongooses on cords. They sat at his feet like poodles while he propositioned our captain.

" 'Sir,' he said, 'you must have many rats aboard after all those days at sea. Would you like to get rid of them?'

"The captain smiled. 'I would indeed!' he says. 'What do you have in mind?'

" 'Rupees,' the Indian said. 'I would take it that you

are a sporting man. My little friends here, the mungooses, will clean out your hold. What would you offer for each dead rat they bring up?'

"The captain looked hard at the skinny Indian and his two gray animals. He laughed. 'Worth a rupee apiece if they can deliver. But I doubt it. Rats in a ship's hold are educated.'

" 'So are my friends,' said the Indian. 'Let us try.' "

The sailor looked at Mr. Magoo. "Amazing what happened then! We went aboard; most of the crew gathered to watch. The Indian turned those mongooses loose. The hold was opened, and they went quick as light below. One of the men timed it. Every eight minutes they came back, one at a time. With a dead rat in their mouths! Laid 'em right at the Indian's feet! And went back for more. When the captain, standing there with his mouth open, counted ten dead rats in not much over an hour, he began to allow that he would rather have what rats were left in the hold and keep his rupees. He quickly counted out the ten rupees. The Indian made a hen-cluck sound in his throat and the mongooses came out of the hold. He slipped the cords on them, smiled, tucked the money in that white thing around his waist, and off they went."

The sailor looked at Mr. Magoo again. "Amazing little beggars!"

On another afternoon Lloyd Hackl walked over beside a slender, gray-haired lady who stood by Magoo's cage.

"Aren't you the nice little fellow!" she was saying. "Just like my Tikki. Only he was larger. My, but you're handsome!"

She glanced at Hackl. "I used to be a Presbyterian missionary years ago in India and had a fellow just like this. Wonderful animals. Full of fun. Make better pets than any other animal I know. Terribly active, though. Mine crawled in bed and tickled my feet to wake me up every morning—at exactly six o'clock, his breakfast time. Did it for years. Nearly lost him once when I was packing a box of gifts for the family in the States. I was just about ready to give it to my 'babu' to mail when the box began to jump. It was my Tikki. He had gotten in without me seeing him."

She cooed to Magoo. "Did you know that they were good watchdogs?"

Hackl shook his head encouragingly.

"Yes," she said. "They have a protective feeling for the people they love. Tikki would chase intruders from the mission, screaming at them and bristling up. Once he routed a dog fully twenty times his size.

"During the rainy season we were bothered by scorpions. You know those biting insects that poison? Well, Tikki loved them. Didn't seem to worry about being bitten, either. My assistant called them 'Tikki's walking candy.' Anyway, he kept our place free from the horrid things."

She stopped, clucking affectionately at the mongoose.

"How old is your Mr. Magoo?"

"We don't rightly know, ma'am. A sailor from an English ship gave him to us a few weeks ago. He's young, though. I examined his teeth. Maybe two or three at the most."

She stood talking to Mr. Magoo for a few minutes, then turned brightly, said good-bye to Hackl, and left without looking at another animal.

A few days later it was discovered that the zoo's star attraction had developed a new habit. After his meal Mr. Magoo sat and picked his teeth with a claw on his right front foot. An amusing, even absurd sight, it reminded those who saw it of a portly old gentleman using a toothpick after a sirloin steak dinner.

The chain of circumstances that would bring a death sentence to Mr. Magoo and launch this country's most widely publicized battle for the life of an animal began with its first link the monthly meeting of the Arrowhead Zoological Society, the organization that sponsored the zoo and conducted its business. Meetings are held the first Wednesday of every month. This one was at City Hall, with fifteen directors attending.

As usual, reporters were there, hoping to pick up an easy animal story, those appealing items that practically write themselves.

The meeting droned on with the usual discussion of repairs to be made, animals to be bought, and the constant complaint that it was getting more and more difficult to run a zoo of this size on the $41,000 annual budget that Lloyd Hackl received to maintain the place and its five employees.

Afterward, as the directors talked, the reporters moved among them, asking questions.

"Anything new and interesting in your zoo?" Hackl was asked.

Before he could respond, the Society's president, Dr. Pershing Hofslund, said, "Don't forget the mongoose. He's an interesting little fellow."

"Mongoose?" said the reporter. "What exactly is that?"

As Hackl told him, the reporter, William F. Thompson, took notes and made an appointment to see the mongoose at the zoo the next day.

The story appeared in the morning paper, the *News and Tribune,* on November 13, 1962. Accompanying it was a photograph of Lloyd Hackl, with Mr. Magoo on his shoulder, an appealing shot taken by staff photographer George Starkey. Soon it would appear in more than three hundred newspapers throughout the country.

With a bold two-column head, the story had prominent placement on the front page:

## TOUGH ON COBRAS
### Tea-Drinking Pet Feared

There's a tea-drinking mongoose at the Duluth Zoo. Tea with sugar, that is, which might make the little weasel-like animal sound pretty tame, but in India, the deadly cobra fears only one animal: the mongoose.

And with good reason. In a fight, the mongoose, usually no more than 16 inches long, will kill the six-foot snake, breaking its neck after a furious struggle.

It is the first mongoose ever on display in Duluth, and Zoo Director Hackl thought possibly it is the only mongoose in captivity in the United States.

Its life at the zoo thus far has been without the hazards of jungle survival. In fact, Hackl said, "this is really a house pet. It eats a little meat and vegetables and drinks a little milk. Its favorite is warm tea with sugar."

The public can see the mongoose, at rest if not at war, from 10 A.M. to 4 P.M. daily, the zoo's winter hours.

The story that went into dramatic detail on the mongoose's snake-fighting abilities caused much comment.

The evening paper, the *Herald,* ran a follow-up on the front page that night:

### MONGOOSE HAS SWEET TOOTH

The new mongoose at the Duluth Zoo has displayed a taste for warm tea—with sugar, please.

Lloyd Hackl, zoo director, said the animal is the first mongoose ever displayed in the city. It was the pet of a foreign sailor who gave it to Hackl when the ship docked in Duluth recently. Hackl says it drinks milk but prefers tea.

The mongoose, native to India, fearlessly attacks and kills most poisonous snakes.

Among the residents of Duluth who read both stories with interest was Clarence L. Bingham, Assistant Collector of U. S. Customs. After the first story in the morning paper he called Customs Marine Officer Donald Grimwood.

He asked if Grimwood had read about the mongoose in the *News and Tribune.*

Grimwood said that he had.

"A violation of U. S. Code, Title 18, paragraph 42," Bingham said. "I happen to know without checking because I was working as an agent in Pembina, North Dakota, when we refused a shipment of mongooses and seized the animals."

He asked Grimwood to investigate. The Marine Officer

called Harry W. Nash, Director of the Duluth Department of Parks and Recreation, which includes the zoo
among its projects.

Nash, a young executive who respected the talents of
others, left the day-to-day running of the zoo to Lloyd
Hackl. He knew about the mongoose, had been over to see
Mr. Magoo several times, and like everyone else in the
place, was taken with him.

He asked the Marine Officer if Magoo would be con-
fiscated, and was told that he would be. Grimwood said
that he had been instructed by Assistant Collector Bingham to inform Nash to consider the mongoose seized by
United States Customs. It was to be held under lock and
key for their disposition.

Donald Grimwood also advised Nash that the next step
would be a report of the violation of the U. S. Code to
Floyd Davis, Regional Supervisor of Management and Enforcement of the Fish and Wildlife Service, Department of
the Interior, in Minneapolis. Davis, he said, would have to
order the mongoose destroyed.

Disturbed, Nash wanted to know if there wasn't something he could do to circumvent this, saying that Hackl
and everyone at the zoo would be shocked and that there
had to be some solution.

Grimwood had a suggestion. "Why don't you write

Davis in Minneapolis and ask for a permit to keep the mongoose? It's worth trying."

Nash did this immediately, in a plea for the life of Mr. Magoo, telling the Fish and Wildlife official how important the mongoose was to the zoo and its visitors, that it was a single animal, that it would be kept under close observation, couldn't possibly breed or reproduce, and far from being a menace to the country, was an asset.

Reaction was chillingly official:

"Reference is made to your letter relative to the acquisition of a mongoose by the Duluth Zoo," it went. "We are sorry to advise you that there is no way in which we can authorize you to keep the animal. Federal regulations prohibit the import or possession of this animal in the United States.

"We are requesting U. S. Game Management Agent Harry Pinkham to take charge of this animal, have it humanely killed by gas chamber or otherwise, and to transport the body intact to the Regional Office in Minneapolis for disposal.

"We would like to have some photos taken of the animal before it is killed."

Nash's next step was to inform Lloyd Hackl. When he had finished the distasteful task, the zoo director snapped, "We must fight it!"

Afterward Hackl remembers saying that he had been a law-abiding citizen all of his life, but this time he wasn't going to stand by and let the law take its course.

"This time the law is wrong," he said. "Our mongoose will *not* be put in a gas chamber!"

He tried to explain to Harry Nash that it is impossible to live under the same roof with animals without achieving communication with them.

"To use a zoo word, Harry," he said, "most of us who work with animals find it impossible not to anthropomorphize. They become characters to us. And friends. Magoo is like one of the staff."

John Mealey remembers his feelings when he heard of Mr. Magoo's death sentence. "Before I came to the zoo I was a swimming instructor at the YMCA," he says. "Those were wonderful youngsters. I was mighty proud when they won swimming contests—and sad as if they were my own when anything happened to them. But I never felt more shock or sadness than when we heard that news about Magoo."

It isn't certain who gave the story to the press. Many think Lloyd Hackl did. He isn't saying. But it is a fact that he was the best friend Mr. Magoo had and a leader in the complicated fight to save the little mongoose's life in the frustrating days that lay ahead.

He is a good man to have on your side. Not much of a talker, he believes in doing things and letting others make the conversation. He won't take inefficiency. When he got tired of secretaries' mistakes he went to a business school and learned to type. A taxidermist and field naturalist of repute, he came to the zoo after having been approached four times by civic groups, then accepting the post because he sincerely liked animals. Until he took over on March 20, 1956, the zoo directorship had been political, changing every time a new mayor was elected, which made it difficult for any director to accomplish much.

When Hackl assumed directorship the zoo was literally falling apart: its main building needed repairs that would cost more than twenty thousand dollars. On Sundays when visitors arrived they had to walk around pails on the floor placed to catch rain coming through the old roof.

There were few animals: one old lioness, some monkeys, a bear, some elk. Now there is a spectacular variety that the largest zoo in the country could be proud of.

Hackl got them in various ways, using personality and ingenuity. When he wanted a fine young hippopotamus from the Dutch animal dealer Zeehandelaar, he first persuaded the dealer to let him have the $3,400 animal on trial to let the people see it and the city officials realize what an asset it would be.

He then approached his friend Robert Ball of WDSM-TV, outlining the problem.

The result of that meeting was a "Hippothon" on the TV station, a twenty-four-hour nonstop appeal for help to buy the hippo, with orchestras and entertainers offering their services free and cab drivers volunteering to pick up donations at the homes of the givers. The $3,400 was obtained almost overnight.

When heavy iron bars were needed for lion, rhino, and hippo enclosures and the zoo budget was short, Hackl went to his friend Sheriff Sam Owens. The sheriff lost little time approaching the Mesabi Railroad to get discarded track, which was soon fashioned into sturdy cage bars.

So it is assumed that Hackl again went to his friends. The first story on Mr. Magoo's death sentence exploded upon the city on November 15, 1962, in the *Herald*.

The headline screamed, MONGOOSE SEIZED AS UNDESIRABLE. Without a by-line, it was illustrated with a half-column cut of Mr. Magoo:

The Duluth Zoo's tea-drinking mongoose has been nabbed by the U. S. Government as an undesirable alien.

Actually, he has been impounded on orders of customs officials as a violator of a 1900 regulation of the U.S. Fish and Wildlife Service barring the importation into the country of *Herpestes auropunctatus*—mongoose.

The speedy animal, a native of India and noted for its ability to outfight cobras, was given to the zoo by a foreign seaman.

Customs officials acted after hearing that the zoo had the animal.

The city is fighting their action.

Harry Nash, head of the city's recreation department, which runs the zoo, has appealed to the Fish and Wildlife Service for permission to keep the animal.

He said in a letter to F. H. Davis, Minneapolis, Regional Director for the Wildlife Service, that the animal has been "very popular with adults and children and is clean, healthy and well mannered."

Nash said he understood the reason the mongoose isn't allowed in this country is because "it is such a prolific animal." He pointed out, however, that the animal, a male, is minus a mate.

The mongoose, who has a fondness for tea, isn't even aware of what's going on. For want of a better place to keep him, customs officials have him impounded where he's always been —at the zoo.

Unless the government relents, the mongoose will be put to death.

It went on to detail mongoose characteristics and snake-fighting ability.

Minutes after the newspaper hit the streets phones were ringing at the zoo, the newspaper, and at the Mayor's office.

The first indication the Mayor's office had of the seriousness of the situation was when people began filing in and standing accusingly before Miss Alta Marie Johnson, his secretary, as they asked to see the Mayor.

As the office filled she became alarmed and said to a man who was pacing, "What is it?"

He stopped. "The mongoose! We can't let this happen to Duluth! What has that little animal done to deserve a death sentence?"

Bewildered, Miss Johnson asked him what he was talking about. Immediately every person in the office proceeded to tell her. She fled inside to tell Mayor George D. Johnson. He came out smiling confidently, a short, bouncy man in his late forties, dark hair slightly flecked with gray, gray eyes atwinkle behind glasses.

"You're here about the mongoose—" he began, and was stopped with a flood of, "Yes, we must save it!" "It's up to you to help!" "It's a crying shame!" "We'll write Congress!"

When he succeeded in quieting them, he said, "I'll investigate the matter. You have my word that I will take action if I can."

As they left, the phone began to ring; there were fifty calls in less than an hour, with every caller demanding that the Mayor stand up and defend the city's mongoose.

Toward the end of the afternoon it was apparent that the fate of the mongoose had been taken as a personal challenge by a substantial number of Duluth's citizens.

"This is remarkable," the Mayor said to his secretary. "I've never seen anything take hold so quickly. Better get me Hackl at the zoo, and let's see what the story is."

George D. Johnson, Mayor of Duluth from 1953 to 1956, appointed again in 1962 after the death of Mayor E. Clifford Mork, was popular with both political parties. The Scandinavian population liked him because his father was a farmer from Sweden, and the fact that his mother had been raised on a farm a hundred miles west of Duluth gave him strength among the many people in the city who had rural ties.

He had pleased many a citizen of Duluth with a campaign that had nothing at all to do with politics. Several times in a plea to the public he had asked that people send books in memory of the departed to the public library rather than flowers to the funeral homes. "Flowers last a day," he said. "A book with your inscription to the dearly departed will live forever."

He also was an animal lover who was tagged through the corridors of City Hall by his dachshund, and he was a sportsman who had grown up on his grandmother's farm at Aitkin, one of his first memories being the sound of coyotes calling at dawn. He had caught his first trout when he was seven, and tracked his first deer in the snow at thirteen.

So, far from being the city slicker type who thought a mongoose was a word to solve in a crossword puzzle, he was aware of Mr. Magoo; in fact, he was so interested in every aspect of life in his city that he even sat with the Arrowhead Zoological Society at its monthly meetings as a director.

It took twenty minutes for his secretary to reach the zoo.

Hackl was agitated. "I've been trying to get you all day," he said. "The zoo is jammed with people. My telephone has been ringing since early this morning. We've got to do something, your Honor. We can't let this happen!"

"I agree, Lloyd," the Mayor said. "But what can we do? As I understand it, a federal law has been broken. That comes from the top."

"Then we should go to the top," Hackl said. "This is causing plenty of commotion."

"It's too late to do anything today," the Mayor said. "Let's work out something tomorrow."

"Tomorrow" was November 16, and it brought another front-page story, this time in the *News and Tribune*. This report not only pointed up the plight of the mongoose, but also revealed that the Associated Press had become interested and apparently had interviewed Floyd Davis, the Fish and Wildlife official.

### MONGOOSE GIVEN DEATH SENTENCE

The mongoose presented to the Duluth Zoo by a foreign seaman is being sentenced to death for being in the country illegally. Floyd H. Davis, U. S. Fish and Wildlife supervisor in Minneapolis, said he had no choice in the matter, the Associated Press reported late Thursday night.

He said laws prohibit the animal from being kept in the United States mainly because of its ability to reproduce rapidly.

The Wildlife Service agent in Grand Rapids was instructed to go to the Duluth Zoo, pick up the animal, kill it humanely and ship the body to the Minneapolis office.

The animal has been a major attraction at the zoo since its recent presentation to the city.

Zoo officials contended there was no reproduction problem because they just have the one mongoose.

Davis said the animal's carcass would be offered to the University of Minnesota's museum of natural history.

Reaction from the city was so emotional that the Mayor did what many a person with a problem in that state has been doing for years. He telephoned the senior Senator, Hubert Horatio Humphrey, one of the most powerful men in Washington, long a fighter for the underdog. The call resulted in the promise that the articulate Senator understood and would support the Mayor's stand.

The stand was a long consultation with the city attorney, and a telegram to the Secretary of the Interior Stewart L. Udall. It went off early on November 16.

HON. STEWART L. UDALL
SECRETARY OF THE INTERIOR
WASHINGTON, D.C.

THE CITY OF DULUTH ZOO HAS IN ITS POSSESSION ONE MALE MONGOOSE BELIEVED TO BE THE ONLY ONE IN THE UNITED STATES. WE HAVE BEEN ADVISED BY F. H. DAVIS REGIONAL SUPERVISOR MANAGEMENT AND ENFORCEMENT OF FISH AND WILDLIFE SERVICE MINNEAPOLIS THAT THE ANIMAL MUST BE DESTROYED IN ACCORDANCE WITH A FEDERAL STATUTE ENACTED IN 1900. OUR LEGAL STAFF ADVISES US THAT IN THEIR OPINION IT MAY BE POSSIBLE FOR YOU TO MAKE AN ADMINISTRATIVE EXCEPTION IN THIS CASE IF ADEQUATE SAFEGUARDS ARE PROVIDED. SEE TITLE 18 CRIMES AND CRIMINAL PROCEDURE SECTION 42 CHAPTER 3 U. S. CODE ANNOTATED P. L. 86-702 SECTION ONE 74 STAT. 753. REQUEST IMMEDIATE STAY OF EXECUTION FOR MONGOOSE UNTIL LEGAL MATTERS CAN BE RESOLVED. PUBLIC REACTION TO EXECUTION ORDER HERE POSITIVELY FANTASTIC.

                              GEORGE D. JOHNSON
                              MAYOR

The Mayor hadn't waited to take action, as he suggested to Lloyd Hackl. That afternoon, after he talked with the director of the zoo and about one hundred agitated constituents, he called City Attorney Harry E. Weinberg.

He explained what was happening, adding, "And, Harry, I don't want to rush off a wire to the Secretary of the Interior without something more to go on than the fact that the entire city is upset and dead against the execution of the mongoose. He has a job to do, and upholding federal laws is part of it. It would help if you could find something we can hook an appeal on."

The city attorney said he would try. "But I don't think we stand much of a chance," he said. "I'm afraid we're going to have to let the law take its course."

Meantime Lloyd Hackl was having his problems. The zoo was receiving one phone call every sixty seconds, many callers demanding to talk directly to him. Several recommended that Hackl take the mongoose away and hide it until things were straightened out. One man appeared and tried to talk Hackl into letting him take Magoo into his home. "Let them try to get him out of my house," he said. "They'd have to call out the National Guard!"

Hackl was up until past midnight on the sixteenth, the day Mayor Johnson sent the telegram to the Secretary of the Interior, answering telephone calls, seeing people who came to pay "we will support you" calls.

When he arrived at the zoo the next day, there were

triple lines of people waiting at the entrance, many insisting on seeing the director to give him advice. The entire area was so crowded that Hackl had difficulty getting through to the main building. Ten thousand people (one out of every ten in Duluth), most of them adults, came to the zoo this day, Saturday, November 17.

They circled Mr. Magoo, staring and clucking in sympathy, many snapping pictures. Magoo stared back and took the whole business with his usual aplomb, as a celebrity should, but the flash bulbs flaring, the people murmuring and pushing about the area annoyed the great cats: Nemo, the lion, roared; the leopards paced, snarling; the toucans and the mynas chattered; the squirrels ran excitedly about in their treadmills; and the giant anteater began a nervous sniffing through his attenuated snout.

Finally Hackl had to press the caretakers into service as ushers, to ask visitors to say hello to Magoo, then please move on as the number of people, the noise, and the crowding were disturbing the animals.

"It makes them nervous," the caretakers said, Nemo accentuating each delivery with a shattering roar. Despite this, the people kept coming.

Few took time to identify themselves. Most were excited; some were angry.

One agitated old Finn, a fisherman, said to Hackl, "You

are fighting for more than the life of a mongoose. You're fighting for the life of America. We are being governmented to death, being beaten over the head by bureaucracy. Stick to your guns, boy! We're behind you!"

Several women stood and cried before Mr. Magoo's cage. Youngsters trooped by in a somber line.

The *Herald* headlined that day at the zoo, DULUTHI-ANS GO GA-GA OVER ALIEN MR. MAGOO.

The Customs man who had begun it all, thirty-six-year-old Clarence Bingham, slim, sandy-haired, career-dedicated, from Ladysmith, Wisconsin, an Assistant Collector of Customs since 1960, competently tied up loose ends in a letter to Harry Nash:

"You and Zoo Director Lloyd Hackl both have been advised that by virtue of the Customs seizure of this mongoose, all reasonable precautions will be exercised by you and the zoo personnel to insure that it will under no circumstances be released to anyone or be moved to any other location than its present zoo cage, without a specific written order approving such release or move, signed by the Collector of Customs or a Customs officer authorized to act in his capacity."

With this Hackl placed a padlock on Magoo's cage, kept the key in his pocket, and took over the caretaking chores himself.

By this time the city attorney had begun action. Five feet tall, white-haired, at seventy-six Harry Weinberg looked fifty and acted forty. Talented at legal research, powerful in court, he became city attorney in April 1935. Prior to this he had served Duluth for ten years as defense counsel in personal-injury suits, seldom losing a case, saving the city hundreds of thousands of dollars.

A colorful personality, he could recite the poetry of Robert Burns with such an impeccable accent that it was even considered that he become a member of the exclusive Order of Scottish Clans.

He came to the city from Berdichev, Russia, when he was seven, leaving school in the eighth grade to butcher refreshments and newspapers on the Duluth and Iron Range Railroad, the Great Northern and the Duluth, South Shore and Atlantic. Giving this up when he was seventeen, he became a reporter on the old Duluth *Daily Star,* then left to work in the advertising department of the *Daily News* in Sioux City, Iowa. But he liked words better than sales, and returned to Duluth as a reporter on the *News and Tribune.*

An avid reader, he had been encouraged by his fifth grade teacher, Maeta Huntsman, to study the great orators. Pitt, Burke, and Webster convinced him that he wanted to practice law someday. Finally, at the age of twenty-seven, he entered Macalester College, in St. Paul, made up the high school credits he was lacking in one year, then went on to the St. Paul College of Law in 1913, graduating in 1916.

The city attorney didn't find any easy loophole. He didn't get at the research until after dinner, then stayed up late, leaving his study as the city was coming awake, the tugs hooting, the mist rising in gunsmoke puffs from the lake, the traffic beginning to move in a great two-way caterpillar across the Hi-Bridge, linking Superior and Duluth.

Despite a shower and breakfast, his snowy hair was still rumpled, and he had the look of having slept in a boxcar. He walked into the Mayor's office just as the city's top executive was clearing his desk for the day's action.

"I think I've got something," he said wearily. "At least we can play a delaying action on the strength of it."

Mayor Johnson brightened. "You look like you've been all night digging. Thanks for doing it, Harry. What have you come up with?"

Cautious, as most of his professional clan are, City Attorney Weinberg grunted. "I don't expect that the Secretary of the Interior is going to establish a precedent for our mongoose. But at least we can make a respectable plea."

He went on to say that the Lacey Act of 1900, established to protect our wildlife from destructive imports, had been amended in 1960. He read the amendment.

"Paragraph three," he said. " 'Not withstanding the

foregoing, the Secretary of the Interior, when he finds that there has been a proper showing of responsibility and continued protection of the public interest and health, shall permit the importation for zoological, educational, medical, and scientific purposes of any mammals, birds, fish (including mollusks and crustacea), amphibia, and reptiles, or the offspring or eggs thereof, where such importation would be prohibited otherwise by or pursuant to this Act, and this Act shall not restrict importations by Federal agencies for their own use.' "

"Harry, I think you've done it!" the Mayor said. "This could take the noose off Magoo's neck!"

"Don't be so sanguine," the city attorney replied. "There could be plenty of legal murk. Regulations to implement the amended Act may not be established. This was only amended two years ago, and it calls for an intense study of wildlife throughout the world to determine which species are injurious or partially injurious. There is also a difficulty involved in developing effective control provisions to meet the intent and purpose of the amended Act."

"Harry," the Mayor said, "you're making lawyer sounds. But I'm encouraged anyway. I'll get the telegram off, inform the press, and hope for the best."

Before the city attorney left, the Mayor leaned back in

his leather chair and said thoughtfully, "I don't mind admitting that this whole thing is astounding. I've been around this city for a long time. Never have I seen anything become such a tremendous emotional issue. A few days ago few of us had ever heard of a mongoose. Now his life or death is so important that the Mayor of the city keeps the city attorney up all night so we can send a telegram to a Cabinet member, asking him to step around a federal law and free our mongoose!"

"It could only happen in America," Harry Weinberg said, "maybe only in Duluth."

By nightfall the following day twenty petitions circulating in the city had thousands of signatures protesting the killing of the mongoose. Magoo had become the "Duluth mongoose" and residents were up in arms in his defense. The arms, in addition to petitions, were telegrams to Senators Hubert Humphrey and Eugene McCarthy and Representative John Blatnik, and another appeal to the Fish and Wildlife Service, this time by Robert Morris, Executive Secretary of the Chamber of Commerce.

Putting the matter bluntly, Morris asked that a final decision be held up pending a review of the matter. He added, "We would like to get some determination of why it should be such a problem as long as there is only one mongoose at our zoo."

Representative John Blatnik sent a similar request to Floyd Davis in Minneapolis, but that official was undeterred in the performance of his duty. His reply to the new pleas: "The law is unequivocal."

Mayor Johnson stepped back into the fight, asking the city attorney to obtain a restraining order to prevent the Fish and Wildlife Service from killing the mongoose.

The Associated Press released the news that "The Fish and Wildlife agent was on his way to Duluth to carry out his orders to take Mr. Magoo."

The widely circulated Minneapolis *Tribune* ran the story on Saturday, November 17, reviewing the case, sending a man to interview Harry Pinkham of Grand Rapids, Minnesota, the Game Management agent Davis had ordered to seize the mongoose.

"Yes," he said, "I plan on going to Duluth and getting the mongoose, as ordered."

He said he didn't know what action he would take if the zoo refused to turn over Mr. Magoo. "I can't believe that they would do that," he said.

Late on the sixteenth and early on the seventeenth the Associated Press and United Press International released the story of the mongoose's death sentence and a wire photo of Lloyd Hackl with Magoo in that appealing pose on the zoo director's shoulder. Newspapers from California to

Maine picked it up, many running it on the front page. Chet Huntley and David Brinkley brought the plight of Mr. Magoo to the twenty million viewers of their news program. Twenty-four hours after the Mayor had sent his telegram to the Secretary of the Interior, much of America was aware of the drama being played in Duluth. Thousands decided to do something about it.

The city attorney went to the zoo to tell Hackl that he was prepared to defend him no matter what happened. He had advice:

"I wouldn't have given a nickel for the animal's life prior to 1960," he said. "However, there may be a chance now with the revised law."

He advised Hackl to ask officials to talk the matter over before they attempted to carry out the ordered death sentence.

"Keep Magoo under lock and key the way you are," the white-haired lawyer told him. "Unless some foolish person breaks in and takes him, he is safe right where he is. And, Lloyd," he added softly, "he is going to remain safe as long as there is a way we can legally save him. However, we are not going to defy any laws of the United States."

He left, asking Hackl to notify him immediately when Harry Pinkham, the Game Management agent, arrived.

Now Customs came to look at the impounded mongoose. They checked the cage and the lock, admired Mr. Magoo, and for the first time Hackl learned the words of the law that had doomed his mongoose.

A photostat of page 3195, Title 18—Crimes and Criminal Procedure—was brought and read:

42. Importation of injurious animals and birds; permits; specimens for museums.

(a) The importation into the United States or any Territory or district thereof, of the mongoose, the so-called "flying foxes" or fruit bats, the English sparrow, the starling, and such other birds and animals as the Secretary of the Interior may declare to be injurious to the interests of agriculture or horticulture, is prohibited; and all such birds and animals shall, upon arrival at any port of the United States, be destroyed or returned at the expense of the owner. Nothing in this subsection shall restrict the importation of natural-history specimens for museums or scientific collections, or of certain cage birds, such as domesticated canaries, parrots, or such other birds as the Secretary of the Interior may designate. The Secretary of the Treasury may make regulations for carrying into effect the provisions of this section.

(b) Whoever violates this section shall be fined not more than $500 or imprisoned not more than six months, or both.

"This has even been revised several times since 1900," one Customs man said, "revised to tighten the law. The

last time was in 1948—which should be proof enough that there is valid reasoning behind it."

"And again to our benefit in 1960," Hackl said, "at least according to the city attorney."

"We're advised that this amendment hasn't had implementation," Customs said.

They went on pleasantly, recommending compliance with the law of the land, taking the correct line of protocol and least resistance, suggesting to Hackl that he should be extremely careful as the fine and imprisonment could apply to him. One of them asked the name of the sailor who had given the mongoose to the zoo.

"We don't know," Hackl said. "Two of our caretakers picked Mr. Magoo up; the sailor left immediately."

"He is the one who should be prosecuted," Customs said. "We know the ship, of course, but it is doubtful now that anyone aboard her would divulge the name of the sailor. The heaviest fine we can levy on the captain is twenty-five dollars. It is also doubtful whether he would give the name of the sailor at this point."

Hackl said that he didn't see the purpose. The mongoose was here, it belonged to the zoo. The zoo and the city were going to fight to keep it.

"But a law is being broken," Customs said. "This is not good from any viewpoint."

"One male," Hackl said, "kept under lock and key. We have no females. We will get none. Mr. Magoo cannot reproduce. There is no more danger of his escaping than there is of our lions, leopards, polar bears, or monkeys."

"I know," said one Customs man, "but we have learned what can happen when the species that are now prohibited entry do take hold here. Take the starling. In 1890 a Shakespeare buff released sixty pairs in Central Park, in New York. This was part of his poetic crusade to bring to the United States all of the birds mentioned in Shakespeare.

"Now, according to our Washington bird expert, we have over five hundred million of the destructive birds. They destroy fruit crops, contaminate cattle feed lots, roost in buildings in the cities. Do a yearly forty-million-dollar damage to agricultural crops alone."

Hackl shook his head. "I can't see the parallel between sixty pairs of starlings and one lone mongoose."

One Customs man sighed. "I'm glad that this is in the hands of higher authority. If for no other reason than loyalty to a stand and the zoo, your boss ought to give you a raise. But don't let that animal out of its cage until a ruling comes from Washington. You're making yourself vulnerable to prosecution."

Powerful enemies now began to appear. State Representative Willard Munger, a respected member of an old Duluth family, also on the board of the Arrowhead Zoological Society, protested to Lloyd Hackl that the zoo was not complying with one of the fair laws of our land—a law that was put on the books to protect our own wildlife. To reinforce this protest Munger wrote the editor of the *News and Tribune.*

"Sir: The federal laws banning importation of undesirable plants and animals, including the mongoose, are good laws, adopted after careful study. Duluth's mongoose was admittedly smuggled into our country and the zoo by the illegal act of a foreign seaman. If the Interior, Treasury, and Agriculture departments, all of which have some interest in this case, make an exception of Duluth's mongoose, the animal must reenter legally, receiving the rigid inspection required of any plant or animal coming into the country. Anything less than this procedure will make a mockery out of the law. Anyone opposing such a procedure will, in effect, condone violation of health and safety standards we consider essential.

"Duluth's mongoose came from India, where there has been an outbreak of bubonic plague, the worst epidemic disease. Bubonic plague can be transmitted to a human being's body through the bites of a flea or a tick from an infected animal.

"If Duluth can have a mongoose, why can't every other zoo and animal farm in the United States and Canada? Once the precedent is established, sooner or later circumstances will permit mongoose reproduction on this continent. Experience proves that the mongoose, after reducing the supply of rodents and snakes, will destroy poultry, ground-dwelling wild birds, and beneficial small animals.

"Foreign pests are already costing our citizens and taxpayers a great deal of money. Half of the nation's farmers, 63 percent of dairy production, and 80 percent of corn production are in the St. Lawrence Seaway trade area. We had better make sure inspection procedures are enforced to the letter. The economic future of the Midwest depends to a great degree upon impartial federal inspection. We cannot afford to overlook serious violations like the mongoose case. We should thank God that the government has strengthened instead of weakened such inspection."

This intelligent attack sobered Duluthians. Some were especially concerned about this potentially dangerous health aspect and questioned it in letters, telephone calls, and visits to the zoo and the newspapers.

Lloyd Hackl immediately called Dr. John MacKay, who spent several hours examining Mr. Magoo. After comprehensive tests the veterinarian pronounced the mongoose in perfect health. This was reported in the *Herald*, quieting the alarmed.

Now began the battle of the newspapers. The *Minneapolis Star,* the largest daily in the upper Midwest, entered the fray swinging. It ran a blistering editorial, "The Destructive Mongoose."

It cited the West Indies mongoose experiment, but neglected to state that the mongooses had killed the cane rats and saved the islands' sugar cane industry. It didn't mention that the saving to planters effected by the mongooses there was approximately $225,000 each year. The editorial also made the point that wherever the mongoose became established it was a nuisance, overlooking the fact that in their natural habitats, Africa and India, the animals are beneficial.

Ending with the speculative impossibility concerning a single mongoose, it warned, "It would be unfortunate if the mongoose should ever get a foothold in this country. In fact, we are disposed to think that even Mr. Magoo is almost one too many."

Jim Kimball, who wrote a popular column for the Minneapolis *Tribune* came to the defense of the Wildlife official in his city, Floyd Davis, with "Mongoosers, Remember the English Sparrow!" Kimball made the point that undesirable aliens such as the sparrow, the nutria, the starling, and the carp were once considered good guys and are now menaces, warning, "The mongoose might not thrive here, but on the other hand, being a prolific predator, he might do well on our chicken and turkey flocks."

John Mealey was puzzled by the uproar against Magoo. "I don't get it," he said to Hackl. "This is a male mongoose. No females around, you understand. Even if he did escape, what could he do? Freeze to death in Duluth's temperature of 20 below zero? Attack children on the streets? Spread a deadly virus that would turn people to stone? Invade the supermarkets and cause a food shortage? Run to the woods and mate with a moose and create a monster? All the while no one makes mention that zoos have really dangerous animals—and that one of the reasons we have a zoo is to please people, educate the children, and that we make it our business not to let anything escape."

But Magoo's friends outnumbered his enemies:

The *Herald* and the *News and Tribune* were now running daily reports on the Duluth mongoose. Television stations WDSM and KDAL interrupted programs to bring latest developments. Philip Schrader, an announcer on radio station WEBC began a "No Noose for the Mongoose" program. Members of that station even appeared before the City Council, requesting that it enter into negotiations to obtain a reprieve for the mongoose.

On the prime spot, the six o'clock news, just after reports on state politics, General Edwin Walker's impending trial, and Premier Khrushchev's reactions to nuclear testing, came "Some residents of the area have offered money to hire an attorney to seek an injunction in the case of Mr. Magoo vs. The United States."

Thus, by weaving the issue in with national and international news, WEBC kept the mongoose case a daily feature, receiving the enthusiastic support of its listeners.

Telegrams started to pour in. Typical was: SAVE MR. MAGOO, WE ARE ONE HUNDRED PERCENT BEHIND HIM. And: PLEASE LET US KEEP MR. MAGOO. HE HAS DONE NOTHING TO WARRANT DESTRUCTION. HE CAN DO NO HARM TO ANYONE. I FEEL THE LAW SHOULD BE SET ASIDE IN THIS INSTANCE.

Part of the appeal of the "No Noose for the Mongoose" campaign was "The Ballad of Mr. Magoo," written by WEBC disc jockey William McCollough. Sung to the tune of "Davey Crockett," it was warbled by various members of the radio station at least once an hour, pin-pointing the mongoose's problem, becoming more familiar to residents than "The Star-Spangled Banner." It went:

> This is the story of Mr. Magoo
> You may not believe it, but it happens to be true.
> They wanna put a noose
> on Magoo, the mongoose.
> But the people of Duluth wanna keep him in the zoo.

Chorus:

> Mister . . . Mister Magoo
> The lonely little only mongoose.
>
> He can't find a mate in the entire state.
> But still the mighty government has sealed his fate.
> To be quite specific
> They say he's too prolific.
> But what's he gonna do with a lock upon his gate?

Now the radio station and the two newspapers were the receptacles of public wrath. Announcers, reporters, and editors were assailed by telephone calls and letters; people stopped them on the street. "Fan our fire," one man phoned the editor of the *Herald,* "so the country can help us save this poor animal!"

Typical were letters with an admixture of reasoning and disgust:

"Sir: I, too, have been revolted over the ruling of the U. S. Fish and Wildlife supervisor in Minneapolis regarding the little mongoose presented to the Duluth Zoo.

"I believe that one of the faults with present-day society is that people in positions of authority operate by the 'book' without bothering to think things through intelligently and coming to a wise conclusion.

"Since I was around 14 I have known that it takes two

to produce little ones of the same species. Unless the authorities know something about mongooses that the rest of us don't know, it would be impossible to get a wild increase in mongooses—or any increase for that matter—with just one mongoose.

"I hope the people of Duluth find a way out of this disgusting situation. I have not been able to get to Duluth to see him at the zoo, but I very much want to do so. I think it is a distinction for the Duluth Zoo to acquire so rare an animal. I think Duluthians should fight to keep him, especially since the ruling in this case is so stupid.

Disgusted . . ."

"Sir: I understand that the law is directed against this one helpless creature, a mongoose in the Duluth Zoo. Why?

"I have always believed the mongoose to be one of the good guys of the animal world, sudden death to poisonous snakes. It must have occurred to the disciplined governmental mind that Mr. Magoo's presence in the Duluth Zoo constituted an illegal entry as contraband, surreptitiously passed off a foreign ship.

"Among all governments, only deliberate and outright treason ranks as a higher sin. Helpless pawns of their conditionings, they must act on the triggering phrase.

"There is more at stake here than meets the eye.

"How long will it be before some agency, brooding over these matters, begins to look askance and with pursed lips at the Wisconsin muskellunge?

"Who can say that this fighting fish is not an outlaw Canadian export, who, without passport or visa, made entry into these waters via the Great Lakes. What then, Wisconsin?

"What about that little herd of buffalo in South Dakota? A true national breed? Or did a shaggy bull, in some distant past, snort disdainfully at the borderline running through Albertan plains, and jerking his head preemptorily at his harem, step grandiloquently across into U. S. Wildlife Agency territory?

"It becomes increasingly clear that Mr. Magoo must be fought for tooth and nail. If Duluth fails to hold—if Mr. Magoo is sacrificed to governmental decree—then surely the position of the Wisconsin musky must be considered shaky, at best. It may only be a matter of time before bazooka-bearing Wildlife agents move in on that little herd of South Dakota buffalo.

"I urgently suggest that Mr. Magoo be placed under heavy guard and hustled off to a place of safety until the all-clear is sounded.

"An all-clear we must have—else the American Revolution was in vain."

But the recipient of most of the mail was Lloyd Hackl. Correspondence arrived at the zoo by the mailbagful. At first when letters poured across his desk he put them aside, hoping he could find the time to read them later. But as they continued to arrive, he began to realize that they were the voice of the people. Americans were making themselves heard. From every state they were saying, "This is unfair. We do not like it."

Zoo directors wrote telling him that America's 117 zoos applauded his stand, and the Director of Albuquerque, New Mexico's Rio Grande Zoo informed Hackl that it was a matter of record that in Europe there were no controls upon importations of mongooses, that they were even sold in pet shops. Yet, wrote the director, Ivo Poglayen, never had any mongooses escaped or reproduced in the wild there.

This encouraging news was offset by a letter from Frederick A. Ulmer, Jr., Curator of Mammals of the Philadelphia Zoological Gardens. His zoo had also received the gift of a mongoose. But in this case the government had acted swiftly, sending two officers with side arms to collect the mongoose. They left with the dead animal's paws to prove that they had performed their mission.

Letters came in every form, from a page torn from a lined school notebook to an engraved letterhead.

One suggested that Hackl "write a nice warm letter to the father of a charming girl who resides on Pennsylvania Avenue, in Washington, D.C., a man of courage and understanding." Another thought that common sense could help: "I shouldn't think that mongooses are any greater threat to wildlife than other animals such as minks, martens, weasels, and ermine."

Some were sarcastic: "Not even a smart one could reproduce without a mate." "There are other animals called humans who live within these boundaries *that plot* to do much more harm to the country than Mr. Magoo would or could do . . ." "The position of federal officials in this instance appears ridiculous."

Others were disturbed. "God help us all!" wrote one woman. Another pleaded, "Let Mr. Magoo die a natural death!" Many writers thought they could solve the problem with, "I am enclosing a small contribution to help Mr. Magoo." One woman was indignant: "Surely there are laws that allow a zoo to care for animals that are predators?" Others wrote, "If ugly, dangerous, poisonous snakes are kept for the viewing in zoos, I say by all means keep Mr. Magoo for public education . . ." "They are the gamest little animals in the world!" "Repeal the antiquated 1900 law and keep Mr. Magoo . . . !" "Please let me come and steal your male mongoose." ". . . anyone who has read R. Kipling should be given the chance to see this amazing animal." ". . . the City of Honolulu would be glad to take him." The letters kept coming, expressing viewpoints from the calm and the logical to the outraged and the angry. "The most deadly animal we have in the U.S. is that demon Communist, the Russian corn rat," one man wrote. "It is a pity we don't have billions of mongooses here in the U.S.A. and train them to cut these Red Communists' throats."

One writer wanted to arrange a swap: "Please don't kill this innocent pet. I trade you for a native of Japan, hardy male Rhesus Monkey worth $50.00 wholesale. I'll drive up if you let me, to your zoo. I give you a German Fitch to kill to satisfy the Government, the same thing as a mongoose, belong to the weasel family, and save the life of this mongoose, so rare to have in U.S.A."

A woman remembered some humor regarding mongooses: "These two boys were writing to order two of your Mr. Magoos. They wrote: 'Please send us two. Now how do you spell two mongoose? Mongeese or mongii? Oh, well, send us one mongoose and while you are at it send us another one.' "

Della McGregor of St. Paul, Minnesota's public library sent a telegram expressing the thoughts of many regarding Lloyd Hackl's stand:

CONGRATULATIONS. CHILDREN ALL OVER AMERICA BROUGHT UP ON KIPLING'S JUNGLE BOOK AND LOVERS OF HEROIC RIKKI-TIKKI-TAVI WILL BE GRATEFUL TO HAVE YOU COME TO MR. MAGOO'S RESCUE.

The children spoke for themselves. "Dear Mr. Hackl, please don't kill the mongoose," wrote an eight-year-old. An entire class from Silver Springs, Maryland, wrote, "Please save Mr. Magoo!" "I don't see what fault it is of this little animal that he has such a high reproductive rate," penned a schoolgirl from Washington, D.C. A ten-year-old boy gave legal advice: "I think, in fact, I am sure that you can lawfully keep your mongoose, Mr. Magoo. He wouldn't do one bit of harm behind bars, and Americans would be glad to see their first mongoose since 1900." Another boy was certain he had the solution: "I think instead of killing the mongoose you should send him back to India. If the mongoose could defend itself it would rather be home with his family than be in his grave."

Of the thousands of letters from children that arrived on Hackl's desk, he liked one from a six-year-old Duluth boy best: "Dear Mr. Hackl, My big sister is writing this letter. Please do not kill the mongoose. If you kill the mongoose I will cry. Pleas Please please do not let the men kill it.

P.S. I love mongooses . . ."

Some writers, while commenting on the injustice of the law condemning Mr. Magoo, also offered information: "Thought you might be interested in some material I came across on mongooses while reading Mathews and Knight's *The Senses of Animals,* quoted on page 112.

"Quote: 'It is well worth mentioning that mongooses will eat every scrap of mouse or rat so long as it is not pregnant—with the *exception* of the gall bladder. The way in which a mongoose can seize and dismember the body of a rodent and yet leave the gall bladder is a matter for wonder. A great friend of mine, who was a first-class surgeon of high repute, and also a first-class naturalist, the late F. J. F. Barrington, was amazed at this. More than once he saw my mongoose perform this delicate piece of dissection, and in his characteristic way said: "It can do that job a damn sight better than I can!"'

"Save your mongoose! He will be a great asset to the zoo—and America."

Another writer recalled a British mongoose that talked:

"In reading about Mr. Magoo and your fight for his life here in my Chicago paper, I remembered another mongoose I knew about when I lived in London that must have been almost as famous.

"This mongoose, living on the Isle of Man with a farmer named Irving and his wife and daughter Voirrey, was called Gef—an Indian mongoose like our Mr. Magoo.

"Only this one was supposed to be a 'familiar spirit' that spoke nine languages, including Hebrew and Greek, could read, seemed to be clairvoyant, could sing songs by Spanish Jews of Turkey, claimed to be eighty-three years old and turned itself into a cat at will.

"Gef lived in a cupboard in the Irving house, moved about behind the paneling, liked candy, but was irritable and often swore—in English. He sang often, his favorite, a hymn, 'The King of Love My Shepherd Is.'

"Voirrey Irving, the young daughter, saw and heard more of Gef than her parents did, and she claimed that the mongoose often went down from the mountain-top farm and wandered about the village picking up gossip which he passed on to her.

"Captain M. H. MacDonald, a British businessman, went to the Isle of Man to investigate the story of the mongoose in 1932, at the request of his friend Harry Price, a famous occultist, founder of the National Laboratory of Psychical Research. Price himself couldn't go at the time.

"Price discovered the existence of the mongoose from a Miss Milburn of Peel, Isle of Man, who wrote him a letter saying that an animal 'looking like a weasel' had joined a family named Irving at Cashen's Gap, a barren place high in the mountains. This animal, she said, could read thoughts, sing, and speak strange languages.

"Captain MacDonald reported that he did hear a high voice supposed to be the mongoose's coming from behind the cupboard door. Harry Price and R. S. Lambert, editor of the British *Listener,* finally did go to the Isle of Man, and wrote a book about the talking mongoose, *The Haunting of Cashen's Gap.*

"Later, Lambert was called insane because of his part in writing the book and nearly lost his position with B.B.C. He sued Sir Cecil Levita, the man who had ridiculed his connection with Gef, the talking mongoose.

"The case reached the high courts, involving Sir Stafford Cripps, Sir Stephen Tallents, Sir John Reith, the British Broadcasting Company and the House of Commons. It was a world-famous case. Lambert won; slander was proved.

"I don't know whether this also proved that the mongoose on the Isle of Man really talked or not. But they certainly do have the ability to get into high places, don't they? I understand that the plight of your Mr. Magoo has come to the attention of the Secretary of the Interior. I wish him luck."

In addition to the flow of letters, Mr. Magoo was getting the celebrity treatment in full measure, surrounded by admirers, reporters, and photographers, the flash bulbs flaring beside his cage so often that even the big cats became accustomed to the bursting light.

Lloyd Hackl faced with mixed emotions these bleak and confusing days when his government seemed determined to kill Mr. Magoo. "I feel like a reluctant jail warden," he told Mealey. "I'm walking around with the key to his life in my pocket and the feeling that I should help plan his escape—put him on a ship that will sail out of the harbor and take Magoo to freedom."

Magoo frolicked as usual, lay on his back after meals in his usual legs-up thank you, but now much of the fun was ended: they couldn't take him out of the cage for walks or have wrestling sessions in the preparation room. According to the government, the mongoose had to remain under "lock and key."

These were tense days at the zoo as the staff waited for the Game Management agent to come and claim Mr. Magoo, feeling guilt every time they looked at the mongoose and the unfairness of a situation in which everyone felt helpless.

For some reason the agent hadn't appeared or even telephoned. One of the caretakers came up with a solution to solve the problem when he did arrive.

"Shanghaiing worked in the old days," he said. "What's wrong with the boys putting Magoo on a boat sailing for Asia?"

One zoo employee seriously suggested that they work out a sentinel service and signal when they saw anyone coming who looked official. "You can always tell them," he said. "Tight lips, shiny briefcase, walking along like they were in mud. When he comes we just close the zoo. Simple. The door's locked. And nobody gets in." He added, "To cinch it, we put a sign on the door, 'Epidemic! Visiting Forbidden!'"

Another caretaker also had the answer: "We dye the big guinea pig gray. Bet this government man doesn't know what a mongoose looks like. We put this guinea pig in Magoo's cage. When he comes we just say, 'There he is, mister, take him,' and that's that."

They did decide that for the first time the dinner bell would be tolled for another reason: it would be rung the moment the Game Management agent entered the premises, summoning the director immediately to cope with the situation.

Normal routine went on, the animals had to be fed, the zoo schedule had to be observed. Mealey divided his time, as he said, "between his two Indians," the elephant and the mongoose, feeding and brushing Bessie, and mostly acting as a guard for Magoo. The people came in a never-ending stream, asking, "Where's Magoo?"

The dinner bell tolled promptly every day at three

thirty, its clarion call, as usual, bringing the animals alert; the sunlight washed over the golden lions sitting in eternal vigilance at the entrance, the railroad engine stood dead on its piece of track, the deserted park was locked in silence, and there was a spirit of sadness over the place.

"We're walking around like zombies," Hackl told his caretakers. "I know this is a moving testament to the personality of Mr. Magoo, but I think we should cheer up. We have the best defense in the world. The people. They're with us. Let's play this calmly. Watch Magoo carefully, so no one does anything foolish. I'm hopeful we'll save him. Remember, the Mayor and the city attorney are also pulling for us."

Six miles across town, at City Hall, the Mayor wasn't hopeful. Even with the astounding national support and apparent sympathy of press, radio, and television, it didn't seem to Duluth's chief executive and the city attorney that Mr. Magoo had much of a chance. There was an ominous silence from Washington.

The Mayor, his eyes pale gray behind the shimmer of glasses, said, "I haven't even had a routine reply to my wire to the Secretary of the Interior. I know these things take time. But I don't think this silence is good."

"What's that old saw?" Harry Weinberg, his white hair

standing like a cock's comb, said. " 'No news is good news.' "

Mayor Johnson shook his head. "Harry, I'm afraid the little guy would be much better off back in his jungle with the snakes."

"These things can't be rushed," Weinberg replied. "The mills of official Washington grind very slowly indeed. I have no idea what action the Secretary of the Interior will take, but I doubt if he'll come right out and clear the mongoose."

As usual in matters of legal protocol, the city attorney was right. The government's first step didn't exactly clear Mr. Magoo.

The news came, as much of it did these days, from WEBC. Philip Schrader, the announcer who had been pushing the "No Noose for the Mongoose" program, made the announcement early on November 18:

"Duluth, Minnesota—Mr. Magoo, the 'Mongoose Without a Country,' frolicked before overflowing crowds at the Duluth Zoo today as residents of the unemployment-stricken Iron Range gathered for a look at one of their most famous residents.

"The little Indian mongoose finds himself unwelcome because of a 1900 U. S. Fish and Wildlife law which prohibits members of his family from visiting our shores.

"But Magoo boosters felt their cause got a big lift yesterday when Interior Secretary Udall said that he would ask his attorneys to 'Take a good, close look at the law Monday to see if there isn't some way of sparing the mongoose.'

"Orren Beaty, Udall's top assistant, said that the Secretary and other Interior officials 'are hopeful we can stop the execution.

" 'From what we've heard, Mr. Magoo seems to be a good, progressive New Frontier-type mongoose,' Beaty said. 'And I've made some preliminary checks with some of the experts here and they don't think the law necessarily requires that he be executed.' "

In Minneapolis the *Tribune,* running it as a front-page story in its Sunday, November 18, edition, headlined it NEW FRONTIER PROMISES AID FOR MONGOOSE, with a three-column cut of University of Minnesota students at Saturday, November 17's Minnesota-Purdue football game holding a fifty-foot white banner with the black lettering SAVE OUR MONGOOSE.

That important home game became a rally for Mr. Magoo, with cheerleaders rooting, "Save our mongoose!" and at the half-time break hundreds of fans marching around under the banner, shouting, "We want Magoo! Let him stay at the zoo!"

The crowds that had gathered at Memorial Stadium to

cheer for their football teams found themselves yelling hoarsely, "Save our mongoose!"

Television cameras panned the parade around the field, the huge banner fluttering its SAVE OUR MONGOOSE plea in the strong November breeze, the students chanting. Once again Mr. Magoo was getting national exposure.

On Monday morning the Duluth *Herald* ran a banner headline: MR. MAGOO, EXECUTIONER, TOO, VERY MUCH AT HOME, with the lead:

The executioner stayed home today. It looks like Mr. Magoo's life may be spared.

Harry P. Pinkham, Grand Rapids, game management agent for the U. S. Fish and Wildlife Service and Mr. Magoo's designated executioner, said, "It would be foolish of me to act while the Secretary of the Interior is still studying the case."

The Mayor and the city attorney were of the opinion that none of the radio or newspaper reports meant much without a written statement from the Secretary of the Interior.

Then the Duluth *News-Tribune*'s Washington Bureau chief, Walter T. Ridder, phoned from the capital.

The *Tribune* headlined his story, MR. MAGOO'S LIFE SPARED: UDALL COMMUTES SENTENCE.

WASHINGTON—The mongoose has been saved!

Late Monday evening the Department of the Interior an-

nounced that a temporary resident's permit has been issued to
the animal. In effect this commuted the death sentence under
which the animal has been uneasily living at the Duluth Zoo.

The matter of the mongoose was settled by the personal in-
tervention of Secretary of Interior Stewart L. Udall, who signed
the reprieve upon the recommendation of the Fish and Wildlife Service, under whose jurisdiction the mongoose falls.

No time limit has been placed upon the residency of the
mongoose, but Udall's order does suggest that when the children of Duluth have sated their appetite for gazing at the mongoose he be deported to India.

The mongoose's difficulties, as it was explained here by the
Interior Department spokesman, is that it has no natural enemies. Every other animal apparently likes the mongoose, so
he propagates himself at a rate which rapidly puts him in the
pestilent class. While other animals don't attack him, he does
not return the favor. Interior Department officials who are responsible for the Virgin Islands and Puerto Rico reported
sadly that mongooses in these U.S. dependencies ate or otherwise did bodily harm to singing birds, ducks, and other of our
fine-feathered friends. They therefore don't want any more
mongooses than necessary.

Under the prevailing circumstances, they don't mind giving
the Duluth mongoose a temporary home, but it was clear from
their tones of voice that they hope he'll soon go back to India.

In Minneapolis, Floyd Davis, the Fish and Wildlife official who had been receiving the brunt of the anger of

the people of his city and Duluth, said, "That's the only thing to do. Send *both* Lloyd Hackl and the mongoose to India."

Developments were rapid. On November 20, Jerald Milon, manager of the St. Paul World Wide Travel Bureau, said that he had made arrangements with Trans World Airlines, booking a one-way passage to Bombay for Mr. Magoo.

Complications arose: friends of the mongoose approached the Indian Embassy in Washington and asked if Mr. Magoo would be welcome in his country.

In confusing fashion the consul built hope up with one hand and slapped it down with the other.

"We have no objections at all," he said. "We have millions of them. I am sure he would be very happy."

He didn't think that he should take the matter up on a government-to-government level, adding, "If a sailor should deliver the mongoose to India by coming ashore with him from his ship, I'm sure Mr. Magoo would be happy and no one would mind."

Then he abruptly closed the door by saying that it would be necessary to have an affidavit from the sailor who had given the mongoose to the zoo, attesting that the animal had actually come from India. This was impossible. The unknown sailor had gone back to sea.

These developments were promptly reported over WEBC and in the *Herald* and the *News and Tribune.* The sad fate of Magoo seemed as imminent as ever to the people. They continued to harass the Mayor and the zoo, demanding just what the Secretary of the Interior would do now that it wasn't possible to send Mr. Magoo back to India. No one knew.

Dayton's Department store in Minneapolis called Lloyd Hackl and offered to deposit a large sum to Mr. Magoo's war chest, "to help in the battle that still lies ahead." The catch: they wanted to exhibit Mr. Magoo in their window for a few days.

Finally the long-awaited letter came to Mayor George Johnson from the Secretary of the Interior. It arrived December 8, 1962.

"Dear Mr. Johnson: This responds to your wire dated November 16th, 1962, concerning a male mongoose in the possession of the Director of the Duluth Zoo.

"Section 1 (a) (1) of the act of June 25, 1948, as amended (18 U.S.C., sec. 42), prohibits the importation of the mongoose and certain other mammals and birds into the United States, its territories, the District of Columbia, and the Commonwealth of Puerto Rico. Section 1 (a) (3) of the act, *supra,* provides:

"(3) Notwithstanding the foregoing, the Secretary of the Interior, when he finds that there has been a proper showing of responsibility and continued protection of the public interest and health, shall permit the importation for zoological, educational, medical, and scientific purposes of any mammals . . .

"In the early part of November a mongoose was imported into this country and donated to the Director of the Duluth Zoo. In accordance with the above act, a United States Customs Inspector advised the Director of the Zoo that he would have to acquire a permit from the Bureau of Sports Fisheries and Wildlife of this Department in order to keep the mongoose. The Regional Office of the Bureau advised the Director that the mongoose should either be destroyed or returned to the country of origin. These instructions were based on a long history of predation on wildlife and domestic poultry in the countries where the mongoose was introduced.

"After further review of this matter it has been determined that it would be to the public interest and not injurious to the public health to permit the Director of the Duluth Zoo to possess this mongoose temporarily. Accordingly, the Director of the Duluth Zoo will be authorized to retain the mongoose until March 1, 1963.

"We appreciate your interest in this matter.

Sincerely yours,
/s/ Stewart L. Udall
Secretary of the Interior"

Mayor Johnson immediately called the city attorney and Lloyd Hackl.

Hackl was cautious when he heard the news. "What happens after March 1?"

"Let's face that when it arrives."

"I don't want to sound like a poor sport," Hackl said. "But if anything happens to Magoo now after all this, I'll have to resign as director of the zoo. This place would be a morgue. I'm told the rest of the employees feel the same. If Mr. Magoo loses, your Honor, you may have to swear in Nemo, the lion, as new director."

The Mayor laughed. "Lloyd, don't worry. This is a game I know how to play. It's called 'foot-knee-hip in door.' First you get the door ajar with the foot, then insert the knee, finally the hip. Then the door is open and you're home free. This reply from the Secretary of the Interior reprieving Mr. Magoo until March 1 is the foot. The door is beginning to open."

One bitter day in January, when the city lay under a pall of ice and snow and winds came off Lake Superior chilling Duluth to 25 below zero, Mayor Johnson called his secretary, Miss Johnson, with a question.

That pert little woman with her straw-blonde hair, her Swedish-blue eyes, and her going-to-a-fire walk was slowing down slightly under the deluge caused by the Duluth mongoose: the phone calls, the visitors, and the letters, always the letters that seemed to come in a river to their door. And she was still having trouble understanding the situation caused by this foreign creature in the zoo. "It's because people are essentially kind, I guess," she told the Mayor one day when he questioned her. "I really don't know. Until this happened I would have said a mongoose was some kind of a bird. But I'll tell you, I'm getting a liberal education in mongooses! Just ask me a question. If I haven't got the answer I'll phone the *Herald* or the *Tribune*. Every reporter there is a mongoose expert."

"I'm wondering," the Mayor said to her this day, "do you think the Secretary of the Interior is getting the kind of mail we are on this? It's important. If he is, it could make the difference."

Miss Johnson smiled. "Your Honor, I would say that *anyone* who could do *anything* for Mr. Magoo is getting letters these days."

Miss Johnson was right. The office of the Secretary of the Interior was in a flood tide of letters. As a result of the news stories mentioning the Secretary's name that were still appearing in many papers throughout the country, he was receiving so much correspondence that he had to turn the matter over to an assistant who was put in charge of the Magoo case.

On January 7, Mayor Johnson himself wrote a letter to

Stewart L. Udall, summing up the case of the Duluth mongoose and asking permission for the zoo to keep Mr. Magoo until May 1.

Mayor George D. Johnson had his knee firmly in the door. His request was granted by the Secretary of the Interior.

In the days to come he would try the hip, then Mr. Magoo would be home free.

Sometime after it was all over and it seemed certain that the Duluth mongoose was safe, Lloyd Hackl came down from his office and walked into the preparation room. Several caretakers were gathered, drinking coffee and watching Mr. Magoo carefully inspect each key in a large key ring that Mealey had placed on the table, a trick the caretaker had learned would keep him occupied.

It was a dark afternoon, with the rains that clear winter coming hard and cold, and the animals restless, pacing under the drumbeat on the roof.

Hackl, his hair a shimmer of silver under the overhead light, was smiling.

"Boys," he said, "it looks like we're in the clear. Got a release here in my hand from the United States Department of the Interior. Dated for release April 20, 1963. I won't go into all of it. We know what it says by heart. But its headline should interest you. 'MONGOOSE AT DU-LUTH ZOO GETS FULL FEDERAL PARDON,' it says. The Secretary himself ends with, 'There can be no threat of an excess of mongooses being loosed in Duluth as long as Magoo is not two.' "

After the noise died he said, "I'd also like to read a letter that came today.

"It says, 'Congratulations on your victory. I just want to tell you that I think there is much more here than meets the eye. There can be little wrong with a people who fight for the life of an Indian mongoose at a time in our history when Russia is rattling the nuclear sabers of war, there is turmoil and trouble in the Far East, unrest in Washington, unemployment. Mr. Magoo is alive today because we in this country have the heart and courage to fight unfairness. If the Duluth mongoose could talk he would thank these people for saving him.' He just signs this, 'Proud,' " said Hackl.

Someone, probably Mealey, said, "He forgot something. If Magoo could talk he would also thank someone else."

"Who?" said Hackl.

"Our government. For listening."

It was Monday afternoon, September 23, 1963. The sun was lemon-yellow, and fog, drifting over the city, finally came from the great inland sea in such constant waves that Duluth looked as if it were afire, billowing in smoke.

The people are accustomed to fog: it blankets their area often. This time it was different: someone important to their welfare and future was coming to Duluth for the first time. As they walked the streets and peered from windows, many looked to the sky and sighed, hoping the blinding fog would vanish in the night.

Next morning much of it had burned off, patches of blue sky showed, and Lake Superior was visible, lying below the city in a great dull gray sheet. Now rain fell into the remaining smoky streaks the way sunlight strikes growing things, bursting the fog into small white buds that quickly flowered, then flowed away in mist.

At two forty-six in the afternoon a blue-and-white 707 Boeing jet transport plane circled Duluth International Airport, gliding in over the run, making its landing as gracefully as a sea gull comes to rest on water. It was emblazoned with the great seal: a bald eagle, wings spread, a ribbon in its mouth imprinted with *e pluribus unum,* grasping in its talons the arrows of war and an olive branch of peace. THE UNITED STATES OF AMERICA was boldly lettered across the body of the plane. As it finally came to a stop on the rain-polished runway, six of Duluth's Air National Guard rolled out the special ramp borrowed from

Andrews Air Force Base for the visit. First out of the plane were two airmen in blue uniforms who stood stiffly at attention as Minnesota's Governor Karl F. Rolvaag boarded the jet.

He emerged seconds later, preceded by the young President of the United States in a gray suit and brightly striped tie, hatless as usual, with a smile as natural as his wave to the people, who surged closer to shout, "Hiya, Jack! Welcome J.F.K.!"

Rain glistening in his hair, John Fitzgerald Kennedy strode into the crowd, shaking hands, telling the people that he was happy to be in their city. After him came members of his Cabinet, Congressmen, Senators, Governors, who then entered the calvacade of cars and made the slow ride behind the President through the rain to the cheers of fifty thousand spectators.

Among the members of the Cabinet was the Secretary of the Interior, Stewart L. Udall, a man who had taken on a hero image for the people of Duluth.

Later, when the speeches had been made and the business of state was over, reporters crowded around the President and his Cabinet. After the news session Secretary Udall, a slender, muscular young man with a wind-burned face and cropped dark hair, asked about Mr. Magoo and how he was getting along at the zoo.

He told the press that when he had first heard of Mr. Magoo he was somewhat amused, but soon realized that the national interest on behalf of the mongoose demonstrated the public's love of wildlife.

"I received letters from everywhere," he said. "People were really concerned about Mr. Magoo. They wanted to save his life."

He noted that the mongoose reproduces rapidly and sometimes destroys other animals and birds.

"If there had been more than one mongoose, they could have reproduced," the Secretary said. "But Duluth had the only one in the nation. I realized that he could cause no harm. Despite the law, I spared Mr. Magoo's life.

"I'm happy he is contented at the zoo, and that the people of Duluth are so proud of him."

When President Kennedy, who missed little in the affairs of his nation, heard about the mongoose and the involved battle to save his life, he was intrigued.

Jesting about it in his deft and charming way, he suddenly became serious and went, as usual, to the heart of the matter.

"Let this story of the saving of Mr. Magoo stand," he said, "as the classic example of government by the people . . ."

. . .

Today America's most famous animal is at the height of his popularity. Two hundred and fifty thousand fans visit Mr. Magoo at the zoo every year. He receives more Christmas cards than most people, eats steak and drinks tea every day, and seems happy—perhaps even happier than he was in those days that now seem so long ago, when he scampered along the jungle paths in India.